Journeys

in Literature and Nonfiction

7

K12 Summit
CURRICULUM

Book Staff and Contributors

Margaret Thomas   *Supervising Content Specialist*
David Shireman   *Manager, Instructional Design*
Steve Mawyer   *Senior Media Editor*
Tim Mansfield   *Writer*
Susan Raley   *Text Editor*
Tricia Battipede   *Senior Creative Manager*
Jayoung Cho   *Cover Designer*
Caitlin Gildrien   *Print Visual Designer*
Sheila Smith   *Print Visual Designer, Cover Designer*

About K12 Inc.

K12 Inc. (NYSE: LRN) is driving innovation and advancing the quality of education by delivering state-of-the-art, digital learning platforms and technology to students and school districts across the globe. K12's award winning curriculum serves over 2,000 schools and school districts and has delivered millions of courses over the past decade. K12 is a company of educators providing online and blended education solutions to charter schools, public school districts, private schools, and directly to families. The K12 program is offered through more than 70 partner public schools, and through school districts and public and private schools serving students in all 50 states and more than 100 countries. More information can be found at K12.com.

ISBN: 978-1-60153-515-3

Printed by LSC Communications, Crawfordsville, IN, USA, May 2020

Journeys
in Literature and Nonfiction

7

K12 Summit
CURRICULUM

Table of Contents

Reading and Writing for Life

Telling Stories

Avenues to Understanding

Instructing, Enlightening, and Persuading

What's Important

Powerful Expression

Influential Words

Reading and Writing
for Life

The Three Brass Pennies

a Chinese legend
retold by Augusta Huiell Seaman

It is in the good old-fashioned way that this fairy-story begins—as all such stories should—Once upon a time. And a very long time ago it was, in the faraway city of Wang Po, in that faraway country, China.

Within this city lived a young man, Ah Fo by name, who was poor in worldly goods, but of a rarely studious and thoughtful turn of mind.

One fine day it chanced that he was walking through the forest outside the city, thinking deeply on existence and the universe in general, when he came suddenly face to face with a huge spider web stretched across the path, in whose silky meshes a bee was wound and struggling vainly to be free, while an ugly spider sat in the center and watched its **fruitless** efforts.

....

fruitless useless

Many might have dodged the web and **sauntered** on, leaving the **hapless** bee to its fate, but Ah Fo was not of this nature. He could not pass a helpless creature in trouble, if it was in his power to assist. **Gingerly**, therefore, he took an end of his cotton robe, extracted the bee from the web, and then, not daring to leave it near its enemy, so exhausted was it, he carried it to his home in the city.

There he placed it on his writing table to recover, while he himself sat down to resume his interrupted thoughts on philosophy. While he was so occupied, the bee slowly regained its strength, crawled to a cake of wet India ink, which the Chinese use for their writing instead of our liquid variety. There it remained standing for a moment, perfectly still. Then it **lit** on a sheet of blank paper. After that, it spread its wings and flew out of the window, quite **unperceived** by the dreaming Ah Fo.

It was when that young student awoke from his **reverie**, however, that a surprise awaited him. Looking about for the lately rescued bee, he could perceive no sign of him. But there before him, on a sheet of white paper, directly in the center where the bee had stood, was printed in fresh ink the Chinese character representing the word *Gratitude!*

....

sauntered strolled
hapless unlucky
gingerly very carefully
lit landed gently
unperceived unnoticed
reverie a daydream

It was an astonishing moment for Ah Fo. How the symbol had come there, he could not imagine; yet he could not but attribute it in some manner to the lately rescued insect. He spent the remainder of the day **cogitating** upon the question and lay awake half the night **bewildered** by the mystery. Early next morning, however, a solution arrived, for a note was sent to him, which read:

> *There is a reward awaiting you, Ah Fo, for mercy to a tiny creature in desperate plight, if you will call today at the fourth house on the Street of the Purple Lantern.*

Naturally, Ah Fo let no grass grow under his heels in seeking out the street and house designated. Here he found an old, old man, living in the utmost simplicity, who shook hands with himself within his **voluminous** sleeves (as is the Chinese custom of greeting) and bade Ah Fo to enter and be seated. When the young student had done so, the old man seated himself opposite and began:

"I know that you are bewildered by the affair which happened yesterday, but I will at once **dispel** the mystery. I am a magician. Through all these many years, I have

....

cogitating thinking intensely
bewildered completely confused
voluminous full and billowing
dispel to get rid of

devoted my power to the relief of suffering and the betterment of humanity. Long have I been pursued, however, by a fellow magician, more **subtle** than I and entirely **unscrupulous**, who would rid the city of me because I have been accustomed to undo much of his evil by my merciful arts.

"It has been well understood that, should he ever lure me into his clutches, my life would be **forfeit**, unless some kindly soul would rescue me. In that case, his power over me would vanish forever. Yesterday I changed myself into a bee, in order to fly quickly to some distant city where I was needed. He must have been spying upon me, for he changed himself into a huge spider, and in the forest, where I settled to rest awhile, he caught me in his wicked web. It was the first and only time this had ever happened, and I gave myself up for lost—when you appeared, and broke his spell over me forever.

"Now, I have little in worldly goods with which to reward you, but I have the power to make you rich and successful, provided you use my gift properly and with **discretion**. Here are three brass pennies. They do not look any different from our ordinary money" (and indeed they did not, being simply the brass Chinese "cash" with a

....

subtle crafty
unscrupulous lacking morals
forfeit lost
discretion care and judgment in decision making

square hole in the middle of each), "but they are magic pennies, and he who possesses them may have a wish for each. This wish he may enjoy just so long as he keeps the penny in his possession, but he loses it, should he part with the coin. Only by mentioning these wishes to me, however, may they be attained."

Then the magician spread out the three pennies before him on the table and stared thoughtfully at Ah Fo through his great, square, horn-rimmed spectacles. "Let us now see," he began. "You will desire, no doubt, an unlimited supply of gold and jewels, a huge castle in the best part of the town, and the beautiful daughter of the emperor for your wife?"

He was about to touch the first penny with his forefinger, when Ah Fo raised his hand.

"A moment, I pray you!" began the student. "This is too serious a matter to be decided so speedily. I feel that the possessions you suggest might not be pure joy. Allow me, if you will, to go home and think this matter over. Tomorrow, after due consideration, I may be better able to come to a decision."

The magician smiled a **benevolent** and delighted smile. "I have not seen so much discretion and **forethought** in many a long day!" he exclaimed. "Go and consider the

....

benevolent kindhearted
forethought thinking ahead

matter, by all means, and may **Confucius** guide your meditations!"

And Ah Fo took his departure.

The next morning he was early at the magician's house. "I have carefully considered the matter, O wise and generous one!" he announced.

"And what might your decision be?" asked the magician, as he spread out the three brass pennies before him.

"I would ask first," went on Ah Fo, "for the power to read accurately the thoughts of others; secondly, for the power to foretell my own future at least a month in advance of any given moment; third, for the power to acquire all learning without any effort!"

When he had finished, the magician sat back with a gasp, took off his spectacles and wiped them, put them on once more, and stared at Ah Fo in astonishment and not a little dismay. "This is most unusual," he stammered, "not to say somewhat dangerous! Have you duly considered, my son, the extent of all you ask?"

"I have duly considered," replied Ah Fo, "and I feel that nothing but these demands can satisfy me, if you intend to be so good as to grant any wishes. I have no others."

"Very well, then," agreed the magician, reluctantly, and he touched each penny before him, murmuring something

....

Confucius an ancient Chinese philosopher known for his wisdom

in a language unknown to Ah Fo. Then he handed them to the young man, bidding him fasten each securely about his neck and touch the proper one of them when he made any of the three wishes. And he carefully indicated the wish represented by each penny, for they all bore slightly different markings.

"And now may I inquire what you intend to do?" asked the old man, curiously.

"I intend to go out and see all the world, acquire all wisdom and possibly, at the end, overthrow this **dynasty** and become ruler of the Celestial Kingdom myself!" announced Ah Fo, grandly.

"You are perfectly equipped to do so. I wish you all success!" smiled the magician. But he gazed after the young man somewhat sadly as Ah Fo walked away. "Come back and see me, I beg, when you have attained your purpose!" he called after him.

When Ah Fo reached his home, **elated** by his rare fortune, he packed up his small belongings, in preparation for starting out on his tour of the world. He had decided that he would see his own country before going on to others, so he planned to cross the great river below the city and travel into the southern part of China.

But first, in order to test the power of his pennies, he touched the one enabling him to see into the future, in

....

dynasty a line of rulers of the same family
elated overjoyed

order that he might **ascertain** the wisdom of this plan. To his horror, he saw himself in a small boat, or sampan, on the river in the midst of a violent storm. The sampan was suddenly upset; he saw himself struggling in the waves and finally disappearing beneath the black water!

"This will never, never do!" he cried, trembling at a fate so terrible. "I was fortunate to have thought of looking the matter up before I started. Evidently the southern route is not safe. I will investigate the northern one, though I would have preferred the other." He consulted his penny, but only to behold himself traveling through the mountains, beset by bandits and left dying by the roadside.

Hurriedly he changed his plans again, with the thought of a western route across the country, this time to discover himself lost in a burning desert, parched with thirst, **stricken** with a fever, and perishing alone under the pitiless sun. In a frenzy, he turned to the last resort, crying, "I will cross the seas out of this wretched country and see the rest of the world first!" But again his **prophetic** penny revealed to him a vision of himself captured by pirates and set to work at the **galleys**.

Pale with fright at the dangers he had so narrowly escaped, Ah Fo sat down to consider the matter.

. . . .

ascertain to determine
stricken suddenly overwhelmed
prophetic predicting the future
galleys ships moved mostly by slaves at the oars

"It is plain that fate does not intend me to carry out this part of my program at present," he meditated. "Perhaps it is because I am not sufficiently equipped. Possibly it might be a better plan to acquire all wisdom first, and I will then be better prepared to conquer this kingdom when the time comes. Study was ever a pleasure to me, and there are some knotty problems that have baffled me of late. With my newly acquired power, it will be quite delightful to wrestle with them!"

So he put his house in order once more, got out his books, and prepared for a tussle with a difficult mathematical problem. And as this was plainly the time to try out the qualities of another of his magic pennies, he touched the proper one hopefully. To his delighted astonishment, he read in his mind the working out of the problem and its answer as plainly as though they were written out in the book before him.

"Now this is truly wonderful!" he cried. "It has not taken me one moment to solve what I have been puzzling over for the past month. At this rate, I shall acquire all wisdom in a short week or so. Let us try another!"

He worked feverishly for a little less than an hour, at the end of which he found he had solved every problem in every branch of higher mathematics that had ever puzzled either him or any of the great mathematicians of the land. But, strangely enough, the delight and elation of the feat had somehow vanished.

"It is almost too easy!" he sighed. "It is like reading it out of a book, instead of achieving it after hours of painstaking and unsuccessful work. However, mathematics was never my favorite study. Let us try how it will work with other branches."

All that day he spent over his studies, with the assistance of the magic penny, discovering that the difficulties of each became as simple to him as the reading of a child's primer would seem to an old man. And more and more did the **zest** for the achievement of wisdom and learning, under these conditions, slip away from him. At length he closed his books with a dissatisfied exclamation.

"This power may prove to be very useful later," he **mused**, "but it has taken all the joy from study for me at the present time. Since the acquiring of wisdom is so easy, I need spend little time over it, I perceive. Perhaps it would be just as well, for my next move, to go about the city and visit my friends and try to find out just what they think of me, so I can judge whom I may count upon as supporters when the time comes for me to overthrow the dynasty and assume my place as monarch."

Forthwith he set out to visit his friend Tuan See, anxious to put to the test the powers of the last magic penny. He found his friend with his family, seated at the evening

....

zest enthusiasm
mused thought deeply

meal, and was **cordially** invited by Tuan See to join them at the repast. Ah Fo was about to comply with real pleasure, for he enjoyed a well-spread table and **congenial** company, when his fingers accidentally touched the third penny.

Plainly, as if it had been written on the wall before him, could he read the real, inner thoughts of Tuan See— thoughts which ran very much like this: "I hope that he has to go quickly! I hope that he cannot accept! There is so little of that dish of delicious bamboo-tips, I do not want to share it! And I am weary tonight. I do not wish to talk. He will probably stay till midnight, and I am ready to drop with sleep!"

It was as if Ah Fo had been struck a blow in the face. He could not have imagined such **duplicity** in the heretofore absolutely cordial and devoted friend. And yet, quick on its heels, came the memory that he had not infrequently felt the same way himself. This reading of other people's minds certainly had its inconveniences!

He hastily refused the invitation to dine, saying he had just dropped in to sit a few moments and must hurry on. Then, all the while fingering his third penny, he began to detail to his friend how easily he had solved that day some of the **intricate** problems they had often mused over

---

cordially in a polite and friendly way
congenial friendly
duplicity deceitfulness; being misleading
intricate complicated

unsuccessfully together. And he could not help but feel that Tuan See must be delighted and admire his success.

Tuan See certainly **lavished** upon him, in words, all the praise he had hoped for; yet the telltale penny kept revealing those horridly candid inner thoughts: "What a **conceited** coxcomb Ah Fo is getting to be! I always realized that he could be tiresome, but he was never so much so as now. What do I care how many problems he has solved? I am only interested now in my work and my family. I wish he would go. I wish he would go! I wish he would go!"

Ah Fo rose and bade his friend a good-bye that was almost a sob. Out in the street, tears so blinded his eyes that he could scarcely see his way home. Once there, however, he shut his door and sat himself down to think it over, longing for guidance as he clutched the penny that was to show him all wisdom. Scene after scene flashed through his brain, detailing to him where he had felt precisely the same toward certain friends, Tuan See among them, when courtesy had demanded that he appear most cordial. Had they been able to read his heart, they would have discovered the same thoughts.

"After all, we are but human!" he mused. "Tuan See is no worse than I. But what am I to do now?" He spent the night in considering the question, and in the early

---

lavished heaped generously
conceited full of oneself

morning sought once more the magician in the Street of the Purple Lantern.

"Kind old man," he said, "I beg you to take back these brass pennies. They have brought me nothing but woe, and I quite realize that it was all through my own silly choosing. I desire only to be as I was before!"

The old man looked at him with an understanding twinkle in his eye. "I rather thought it would be somewhat like this," he answered. "I felt that you were overreaching yourself in your desire for power. Better to have chosen the gold and jewels, the stately castle in the best part of town, and the beautiful daughter of our emperor. And, by the way, these can still be yours, if you care to have me change the power of the pennies!"

"No, no, no!" cried Ah Fo, wildly. "With all gratitude to you, I desire none of these things—less now than ever. If you would grant me three wishes, let them, I pray you, be these. Allow me to forget all that I have learned through the **agency** of these terrible pennies; give me a contented mind; and lastly, allow me to return to my studies with a new zest and the determination to rise by my own honest effort above all **obstacles**. It is all that I would ask!"

"It shall be as you say," smiled the magician, tapping him lightly on the forehead. "And for that you do not need

....

agency power
obstacles barriers

the pennies. I can see that they would not have brought you happiness, in any case, since happiness lies within yourself. You had it before I ever met you, and lost it for a time in seeking after less desirable things. Farewell!"

Ah Fo went out into the street, a contented and happy man once more. And the magician, after thoughtfully considering the brass pennies for a time, took them in his hand, walked out to the bank of the river, and hurled them far into its deep, engulfing tide. ❖

Stopping by Woods on a Snowy Evening

by Robert Frost

Whose woods these are I think I know.
His house is in the village, though;
He will not see me stopping here
To watch his woods fill up with snow.

My little horse must think it queer
To stop without a farmhouse near
Between the woods and frozen lake
The darkest evening of the year.

He gives his harness bells a shake
To ask if there is some mistake.
The only other sound's the sweep
Of easy wind and downy flake.

The woods are lovely, dark, and deep.
But I have promises to keep,
And miles to go before I sleep,
And miles to go before I sleep. ❖

Raccoon Olympics

by Anna Chotlos

I'm eleven years old, wearing a hand-me-down tie-dye
T-shirt way too big for me, and soccer shorts—my legs
riddled with welts from black fly bites. My hands still **reek**
of snake musk from spending the morning looking for
snakes in the woods around the lighthouse.

I'm sitting at the picnic table, telling my dad about
all the garter and fox and ring-neck worm snakes I caught,
when the park naturalist, Paul King, stops by to inspect
the live traps under the lilac bushes beside the table.
He pulls the trap out from under the leaves to reveal one
big raccoon.

....

reek stink; smelling strongly of

I like Paul. He has spent every summer in the park for decades and knows everything about Rock Island—he's a walking encyclopedia of its history, geography, plants, and wildlife. My family is spending the week as volunteer **docents** in the island's restored lighthouse. Paul checks on us most days. He tells us where to turn off the official trails to see secret places regular visitors don't get to go, like the coyote dens, and the natural rock windows in the cliffs, and the ruins of the old fishing village. The day before, Paul told me a ghost story about the St. Martin's lighthouse just across the **channel**. A long time ago, the lighthouse keeper's four children got caught in squall in their rowboat and drowned. Paul pointed out a buoy near the tip of the island and told me the keeper's ghost still walks that beach every night with a green lantern, searching for his lost children. That night, I stayed up, peeking out from behind the curtains and saw a green light bobbing over the water, exactly where Paul said it would be.

"It's a state park. Why do you trap raccoons?" My dad also likes talking to Paul. He smiles with his eyes and leans forward, resting his elbows on the picnic table. Paul stops dragging the trap toward his ATV.

"No predators on the island," Paul explains. "When there gets to be too many raccoons, they start to make nuisances of themselves over in the campground."

docents people who act as guides
channel a wide stretch of water joining two larger bodies of water

"What do you do with the raccoons after you catch them?" Dad asks. Paul sits down at the other end of the table.

"Well, we used to release the ones we caught over on Washington Island, but the residents complained." He looks at me carefully. Paul has only four teeth and a white beard that wobbles when he talks. His eyebrows look like albino wooly bear caterpillars. His face reminds me of Abraham Lincoln—**asymmetrical**, homely, wise.

"So, we decided to train ourselves a swim team for the Raccoon Olympics."

I scooch closer, sensing a story

"You ever heard of the Raccoon Olympics?" Paul asks me. I shake my head. He winks. "No? Well, some raccoons are very good swimmers. But we want to find the best for our Olympic team, so whenever we catch one, we have tryouts."

Paul doesn't really say what the raccoons look like when they swim. But my swimming raccoons wear goggles and have special swim caps fitted over their ringed tails to decrease drag. They front crawl through the choppy green waves on Lake Michigan. My raccoons swim with excellent form and breath control, pointing their toes as they kick, and remembering to breathe on alternate sides. I am missing summer swim team practice this week while

....

asymmetrical features on each side do not have the same shape

we stay at the lighthouse. It will not occur to me until I am an adult to wonder if Paul convinced all the kids he could train wild raccoons to compete in swim meets, or if he just made up a kinder explanation for me.

The raccoon in the large Havahart trap beside our picnic table hisses and grips the wire mesh. I had seen raccoons before, staring shiny-eyed into the beam of my flashlight and **skulking** down storm drains, but never up close, in daylight. Raccoon paws look like tiny human hands. I know raccoons can swim. They eat fish and leave little handprints all over the sandy patches of the beach at night. I picture **nocturnal** lap swim sessions, in raccoon-sized lanes with little log floats holding up the lane lines. Even in late June, Lake Michigan is so breathtakingly cold that jumping in the water feels like getting punched in the stomach, but maybe the raccoons' fur helps them stay warm?

"So, to test their swimming, we drive the raccoons out into the middle of the lake and put them in the water. If they're good swimmers, we start training them for the Olympics—every day taking them out a little bit longer— to increase the distance they can swim." The park rangers have an old wooden fishing boat with peeling forest green paint and a partially enclosed cabin topped with a bulky marine radar receiver. I imagine Paul and Ranger Kirby

....

skulking sneaking; moving stealthily
nocturnal active at night

with clipboards and stopwatches, pacing the deck and yelling encouragement, like real swim coaches.

"Unfortunately, we have not found our champion yet." Paul winks again, but he's looking at my dad, not me. Dad catches my eye as if he wants to tell me something, then looks away. I wonder if Dad has heard of the Racoon Olympics before. I'll ask him later. As Paul packs up the trap, I wait until I think nobody else is listening and whisper to the raccoon,

"Good luck little guy! Swim fast!" ❖

Anna Chotlos's writing has appeared in Atticus Review, Sonora Review Online, *and on a square of sidewalk in Northfield, Minnesota. She is a graduate student at Ohio University, studying creative nonfiction.*

Sympathy

by Paul Laurence Dunbar

I know what the caged bird feels, alas!
    When the sun is bright on the upland slopes;
  When the wind stirs soft through the springing grass,
  And the river flows like a stream of glass;
    When the first bird sings and the first bud **opes**,
  And the faint perfume from its **chalice** steals—
  I know what the caged bird feels!

opes poetic form of *opens*
chalice a cup

I know why the caged bird beats his wing
      Till its blood is red on the cruel bars;
For he must fly back to his perch and cling
When he **fain** would be on the **bough** a-swing;
      And a pain still throbs in the old, old scars
And they pulse again with a **keener** sting—
I know why he beats his wing!

I know why the caged bird sings, ah me,
      When his wing is bruised and his **bosom** sore,—
When he beats his bars and he would be free;
It is not a carol of joy or glee,
      But a prayer that he sends from his heart's deep core,
But a plea, that upward to Heaven he flings—
I know why the caged bird sings! ❖

....

fain rather
bough a branch
keener sharper
bosom the chest, especially when thought of as including the heart and emotion

The Story-Teller

by Saki (H. H. Munro)

It was a hot afternoon, and the railway carriage was correspondingly sultry, and the next stop was at Templecombe, nearly an hour ahead. The occupants of the carriage were a small girl, and a smaller girl, and a small boy. An aunt belonging to the children occupied one corner seat, and the further corner seat on the opposite side was occupied by a bachelor who was a stranger to their party, but the small girls and the small boy **emphatically** occupied the compartment. Both the aunt and the children were conversational in a limited, persistent way, reminding one of the attentions of a housefly that refuses to be discouraged. Most of the aunt's remarks seemed to begin with "Don't," and nearly all of the children's remarks began with "Why?" The bachelor said nothing out loud.

emphatically forcefully

"Don't, Cyril, don't," exclaimed the aunt, as the small boy began smacking the cushions of the seat, producing a cloud of dust at each blow.

"Come and look out of the window," she added.

The child moved reluctantly to the window. "Why are those sheep being driven out of that field?" he asked.

"I expect they are being driven to another field where there is more grass," said the aunt weakly.

"But there is lots of grass in that field," protested the boy; "there's nothing else but grass there. Aunt, there's lots of grass in that field."

"Perhaps the grass in the other field is better," suggested the aunt **fatuously**.

"Why is it better?" came the swift, **inevitable** question.

"Oh, look at those cows!" exclaimed the aunt. Nearly every field along the line had contained cows or bullocks, but she spoke as though she were drawing attention to a rarity.

"Why is the grass in the other field better?" persisted Cyril.

The frown on the bachelor's face was deepening to a scowl. He was a hard, unsympathetic man, the aunt decided in her mind. She was utterly unable to come to any satisfactory decision about the grass in the other field.

....

fatuously foolish; silly
inevitable impossible to avoid

The smaller girl created a diversion by beginning to recite "On the Road to Mandalay." She only knew the first line, but she put her limited knowledge to the fullest possible use. She repeated the line over and over again in a dreamy but **resolute** and very audible voice; it seemed to the bachelor as though some one had had a bet with her that she could not repeat the line aloud two thousand times without stopping. Whoever it was who had made the wager was likely to lose his bet.

"Come over here and listen to a story," said the aunt, when the bachelor had looked twice at her and once at the communication cord.

The children moved **listlessly** toward the aunt's end of the carriage. Evidently her reputation as a story-teller did not rank high in their estimation.

In a low, confidential voice, interrupted at frequent intervals by loud, **petulant** questionings from her listeners, she began an unenterprising and deplorably uninteresting story about a little girl who was good, and made friends with everyone on account of her goodness, and was finally saved from a mad bull by a number of rescuers who admired her moral character.

"Wouldn't they have saved her if she hadn't been good?" demanded the bigger of the small girls. It was exactly the question that the bachelor had wanted to ask.

resolute highly determined
listlessly without interest or energy
petulant ill-tempered

"Well, yes," admitted the aunt lamely, "but I don't think they would have run quite so fast to her help if they had not liked her so much."

"It's the stupidest story I've ever heard," said the bigger of the small girls, with immense conviction.

"I didn't listen after the first bit, it was so stupid," said Cyril.

The smaller girl made no actual comment on the story, but she had long ago recommenced a murmured repetition of her favorite line.

"You don't seem to be a success as a story-teller," said the bachelor suddenly from his corner.

The aunt bristled in instant defense at this unexpected attack.

"It's a very difficult thing to tell stories that children can both understand and appreciate," she said stiffly.

"I don't agree with you," said the bachelor.

"Perhaps *you* would like to tell them a story," was the aunt's retort.

"Tell us a story," demanded the bigger of the small girls.

"Once upon a time," began the bachelor, "there was a little girl called Bertha, who was extraordinarily good."

The children's momentarily aroused interest began at once to flicker; all stories seemed dreadfully alike, no matter who told them.

"She did all that she was told, she was always truthful, she kept her clothes clean, ate milk puddings as though they were jam tarts, learned her lessons perfectly, and was polite in her manners."

"Was she pretty?" asked the bigger of the small girls.

"Not as pretty as any of you," said the bachelor, "but she was *horribly* good."

There was a wave of reaction in favor of the story; the word *horrible* in connection with goodness was a novelty that commended itself. It seemed to introduce a ring of truth that was absent from the aunt's tales of infant life.

"She was so good," continued the bachelor, "that she won several medals for goodness, which she always wore, pinned on to her dress. There was a medal for obedience, another medal for punctuality, and a third for good behavior. They were large metal medals and they clicked against one another as she walked. No other child in the town where she lived had as many as three medals, so everybody knew that she must be an extra good child."

"Horribly good," quoted Cyril.

"Everybody talked about her goodness, and the Prince of the country got to hear about it, and he said that as she was so very good she might be allowed once a week to walk in his park, which was just outside the town. It was a beautiful park, and no children were ever allowed in it, so it was a great honor for Bertha to be allowed to go there."

"Were there any sheep in the park?" demanded Cyril.

"No," said the bachelor, "there were no sheep."

"Why weren't there any sheep?" came the inevitable question arising out of that answer.

The aunt permitted herself a smile, which might almost have been described as a grin.

"There were no sheep in the park," said the bachelor, "because the Prince's mother had once had a dream that her son would either be killed by a sheep or else by a clock falling on him. For that reason the Prince never kept a sheep in his park or a clock in his palace."

The aunt **suppressed** a gasp of admiration.

"Was the Prince killed by a sheep or by a clock?" asked Cyril.

"He is still alive, so we can't tell whether the dream will come true," said the bachelor unconcernedly; "anyway, there were no sheep in the park, but there were lots of little pigs running all over the place."

"What color were they?"

"Black with white faces, white with black spots, black all over, gray with white patches, and some were white all over."

The story-teller paused to let a full idea of the park's treasures sink into the children's imaginations; then he resumed:

"Bertha was rather sorry to find that there were no flowers in the park. She had promised her aunts, with

....

suppressed concealed; stifled

tears in her eyes, that she would not pick any of the kind Prince's flowers, and she had meant to keep her promise, so of course it made her feel silly to find that there were no flowers to pick."

"Why weren't there any flowers?"

"Because the pigs had eaten them all," said the bachelor promptly. "The gardeners had told the Prince that you couldn't have pigs and flowers, so he decided to have pigs and no flowers."

There was a murmur of approval at the excellence of the Prince's decision; so many people would have decided the other way.

"There were lots of other delightful things in the park. There were ponds with gold and blue and green fish in them, and trees with beautiful parrots that said clever things at a moment's notice, and humming birds that hummed all the popular tunes of the day. Bertha walked up and down and enjoyed herself immensely, and thought to herself: 'If I were not so extraordinarily good I should not have been allowed to come into this beautiful park and enjoy all that there is to be seen in it,' and her three medals clinked against one another as she walked and helped to remind her how very good she really was. Just then an enormous wolf came prowling into the park to see if it could catch a fat little pig for its supper."

"What color was it?" asked the children, amid an immediate quickening of interest.

"Mud-colour all over, with a black tongue and pale gray eyes that gleamed with unspeakable ferocity. The first thing that it saw in the park was Bertha; her pinafore was so spotlessly white and clean that it could be seen from a great distance. Bertha saw the wolf and saw that it was stealing toward her, and she began to wish that she had never been allowed to come into the park. She ran as hard as she could, and the wolf came after her with huge leaps and bounds. She managed to reach a shrubbery of myrtle bushes and she hid herself in one of the thickest of the bushes. The wolf came sniffing among the branches, its black tongue lolling out of its mouth and its pale gray eyes glaring with rage. Bertha was terribly frightened, and thought to herself: 'If I had not been so extraordinarily good I should have been safe in the town at this moment.' However, the scent of the myrtle was so strong that the wolf could not sniff out where Bertha was hiding, and the bushes were so thick that he might have hunted about in them for a long time without catching sight of her, so he thought he might as well go off and catch a little pig instead. Bertha was trembling very much at having the wolf prowling and sniffing so near her, and as she trembled the medal for obedience clinked against the medals for good conduct and punctuality. The wolf was just moving away when he heard the sound of the medals clinking and stopped to listen; they clinked again in a bush quite near him. He dashed into the bush, his pale gray eyes gleaming with ferocity and triumph, and dragged Bertha out and devoured her to the last morsel. All that was left of her were her shoes, bits of clothing, and the three medals for goodness."

"Were any of the little pigs killed?"

"No, they all escaped."

"The story began badly," said the smaller of the small girls, "but it had a beautiful ending."

"It is the most beautiful story that I ever heard," said the bigger of the small girls, with immense decision.

"It is the *only* beautiful story I have ever heard," said Cyril.

A **dissentient** opinion came from the aunt.

"A most improper story to tell to young children! You have undermined the effect of years of careful teaching."

"At any rate," said the bachelor, collecting his belongings preparatory to leaving the carriage, "I kept them quiet for ten minutes, which was more than you were able to do."

"Unhappy woman!" he observed to himself as he walked down the platform of Templecombe station; "for the next six months or so those children will assail her in public with demands for an improper story!" ❖

....

disentient expressing disagreement

Telling Stories

Charles

by Shirley Jackson

The day my son Laurie started kindergarten he **renounced** corduroy overalls with bibs and began wearing blue jeans with a belt; I watched him go off the first morning with the older girl next door, seeing clearly that an era of my life was ended, my sweet-voiced nursery-school tot replaced by a long-trousered, **swaggering** character who forgot to stop at the corner and wave goodbye to me.

He came home the same way, the front door slamming open, his cap on the floor, and the voice suddenly become **raucous** shouting, "Isn't anybody *here*?"

renounced rejected; gave up
swaggering strutting in a bold, proud way
raucous unpleasantly loud

At lunch he spoke **insolently** to his father, spilled his baby sister's milk, and remarked that his teacher said we were not to take the name of the Lord in vain.

"How *was* school today?" I asked, **elaborately** casual.

"All right," he said.

"Did you learn anything?" his father asked.

Laurie regarded his father coldly. "I didn't learn nothing," he said.

"Anything," I said. "Didn't learn anything."

"The teacher spanked a boy, though," Laurie said, addressing his bread and butter. "For being fresh," he added, with his mouth full.

"What did he do?" I asked. "Who was it?"

Laurie thought. "It was Charles," he said. "He was fresh. The teacher spanked him and made him stand in a corner. He was awfully fresh."

"What did he do?" I asked again, but Laurie slid off his chair, took a cookie, and left, while his father was still saying, "See here, young man."

The next day Laurie remarked at lunch, as soon as he sat down, "Well, Charles was bad again today." He grinned enormously and said, "Today Charles hit the teacher."

"Good heavens," I said, mindful of the Lord's name, "I suppose he got spanked again?"

....

insolently rudely
elaborately with great care; painstakingly

"He sure did," Laurie said. "Look up," he said to his father.

"What?" his father said, looking up.

"Look down," Laurie said. "Look at my thumb. Gee, you're dumb." He began to laugh insanely.

"Why did Charles hit the teacher?" I asked quickly.

"Because she tried to make him color with red crayons," Laurie said. "Charles wanted to color with green crayons so he hit the teacher and she spanked him and said nobody play with Charles but everybody did."

The third day—it was Wednesday of the first week—Charles bounced a see-saw onto the head of a little girl and made her bleed, and the teacher made him stay inside all during recess. Thursday Charles had to stand in a corner during story-time because he kept pounding his feet on the floor. Friday Charles was **deprived** of blackboard privileges because he threw chalk.

On Saturday I remarked to my husband, "Do you think kindergarten is too unsettling for Laurie? All this toughness, and bad grammar, and this Charles boy sounds like such a bad influence."

"It'll be all right," my husband said reassuringly. "Bound to be people like Charles in the world. Might as well meet them now as later."

On Monday Laurie came home late, full of news. "Charles," he shouted as he came up the hill; I was waiting

....

deprived kept from having

anxiously on the front steps. "Charles," Laurie yelled all the way up the hill, "Charles was bad again."

"Come right in," I said, as soon as he came close enough. "Lunch is waiting."

"You know what Charles did?" he demanded, following me through the door. "Charles yelled so in school they sent a boy in from first grade to tell the teacher she had to make Charles keep quiet, and so Charles had to stay after school. And so all the children stayed to watch him."

"What did he do?" I asked.

"He just sat there," Laurie said, climbing into his chair at the table. "Hi, Pop, y'old dust mop."

"Charles had to stay after school today," I told my husband. "Everyone stayed with him."

"What does this Charles look like?" my husband asked Laurie. "What's his other name?"

"He's bigger than me," Laurie said. "And he doesn't have any rubbers and he doesn't ever wear a jacket."

Monday night was the first Parent-Teachers meeting, and only the fact that the baby had a cold kept me from going; I wanted **passionately** to meet Charles's mother. On Tuesday Laurie remarked suddenly, "Our teacher had a friend come to see her in school today."

"Charles's mother?" my husband and I asked simultaneously.

....

passionately with strong emotion; enthusiastically

"Naaah," Laurie said scornfully. "It was a man who came and made us do exercises, we had to touch our toes. Look." He climbed down from his chair and squatted down and touched his toes. "Like this," he said. He got solemnly back into his chair and said, picking up his fork, "Charles didn't even *do* exercises."

"That's fine," I said heartily. "Didn't Charles want to do exercises?"

"Naaah," Laurie said. "Charles was so fresh to the teacher's friend he wasn't *let* do exercises."

"Fresh again?" I said.

"He kicked the teacher's friend," Laurie said. "The teacher's friend told Charles to touch his toes like I just did and Charles kicked him."

"What are they going to do about Charles, do you suppose?" Laurie's father asked him.

Laurie shrugged elaborately. "Throw him out of school, I guess," he said.

Wednesday and Thursday were routine; Charles yelled during story hour and hit a boy in the stomach and made him cry. On Friday Charles stayed after school again and so did all the other children.

With the third week of kindergarten Charles was an institution in our family; the baby was being a Charles when she cried all afternoon; Laurie did a Charles when he filled his wagon full of mud and pulled it through the kitchen; even my husband, when he caught his elbow in the telephone cord and pulled telephone, ashtray, and a bowl of flowers off the table, said, after the first minute, "Looks like Charles."

During the third and fourth weeks it looked like a **reformation** in Charles; Laurie reported grimly at lunch on Thursday of the third week, "Charles was so good today the teacher gave him an apple."

"What?" I said, and my husband added **warily**, "You mean Charles?"

"Charles," Laurie said. "He gave the crayons around and he picked up the books afterward and the teacher said he was her helper."

"What happened?" I asked **incredulously**.

"He was her helper, that's all," Laurie said, and shrugged.

"Can this be true, about Charles?" I asked my husband that night. "Can something like this happen?"

"Wait and see," my husband said **cynically**. "When you've got a Charles to deal with, this may mean he's only plotting."

He seemed to be wrong. For over a week Charles was the teacher's helper; each day he handed things out and he picked things up; no one had to stay after school.

....

reformation a great improvement
warily cautiously
incredulously with disbelief
cynically with distrust

"The P.T.A. meeting's next week again," I told my husband one evening. "I'm going to find Charles's mother there."

"Ask her what happened to Charles," my husband said. "I'd like to know."

"I'd like to know myself," I said.

On Friday of that week things were back to normal. "You know what Charles did today?" Laurie demanded at lunch table, in a voice slightly awed. "He told a little girl to say a word and she said it and the teacher washed her mouth out with soap and Charles laughed."

"What word?" his father asked unwisely, and Laurie said, "I'll have to whisper it to you, it's so bad." He got down off his chair and went around to his father. His father bent his head down and Laurie whispered joyfully. His father's eyes widened.

"Did Charles tell the little girl to say *that*?" he asked respectfully.

"She said it *twice*," Laurie said. "Charles told her to say it *twice*."

"What happened to Charles?" my husband asked.

"Nothing," Laurie said. "He was passing out the crayons."

Monday morning Charles abandoned the little girl and said the evil word himself three or four times, getting

....

awed impressed and filled with wonder

his mouth washed out with soap each time. He also threw chalk.

My husband came to the door with me that evening as I set out for the P.T.A. meeting. "Invite her over for a cup of tea after the meeting," he said. "I want to get a look at her."

"If only she's there," I said prayerfully.

"She'll be there," my husband said. "I don't see how they could hold a P.T.A. meeting without Charles's mother."

At the meeting I sat restlessly, scanning each comfortable **matronly** face, trying to determine which one hid the secret of Charles. None of them looked to me **haggard** enough. No one stood up in the meeting and apologized for the way her son had been acting. No one mentioned Charles.

After the meeting I identified and sought out Laurie's kindergarten teacher. She had a plate with a cup of tea and a piece of chocolate cake; I had a plate with a cup of tea and a piece of marshmallow cake. We **maneuvered** up to one another cautiously and smiled.

"I've been so anxious to meet you," I said. "I'm Laurie's mother."

"We're all so interested in Laurie," she said.

"Well, he certainly likes kindergarten," I said. "He talks about it all the time."

....

matronly mature and motherly
haggard worn-out; exhausted
maneuvered in a stiff, formally proper way

"We had a little trouble adjusting, the first week or so," she said **primly**, "but now he's a fine little helper. With occasional lapses, of course."

"Laurie usually adjusts very quickly," I said. "I suppose this time it's Charles's influence."

"Charles?"

"Yes," I said, laughing, "you must have your hands full in that kindergarten, with Charles."

"Charles?" she said. "We don't have any Charles in the kindergarten." ❖

---

primly in a stiff, formally proper way

The Necklace

by Guy de Maupassant

She was one of those pretty and charming young girls who sometimes are born, as if by a mistake of destiny, into a family of clerks. She had no **dowry**, no expectations, no way of being known, understood, loved, married by any rich and distinguished man; and so she let herself be married to a little clerk of the Ministry of Education.

She dressed plainly because she could not dress well, but she was as unhappy as if she had really fallen from her proper place in life—since with women, there is neither **caste** nor rank, because beauty, grace and charm take the place of family and birth. Natural ingenuity, instinct for what is elegant, and a **supple** mind are their

dowry money given by a bride's family to the groom at the time of their marriage
caste social class based on rank and wealth
supple capable of adapting quickly to new situations; flexible

sole hierarchy, and make of women of the people the equals of the very greatest ladies.

Mathilde suffered ceaselessly, feeling herself born to enjoy all delicacies and all luxuries. She was distressed at the poverty of her dwelling, at the bareness of the walls, at the shabby chairs, the ugliness of the curtains. All these things, which another woman of her rank would never even have noticed, tortured her and made her angry. The sight of the little **Breton** peasant who did her humble housework aroused in her despairing regrets and **bewildering** dreams. She thought of silent **antechambers** hung with Oriental **tapestry**, illumined by tall lamps of bronze, with two tall footmen in knee breeches asleep in the big armchairs, made drowsy by the oppressive heat of the stove. She thought of long reception halls hung with ancient silk, of the dainty cabinets containing priceless curiosities, and of the little **coquettish** perfumed reception rooms made for chatting at five o'clock with **intimate** friends, with men famous and sought after, whom all women envy and whose attention they all desire.

....

sole only
hierachy a grouping or ranking into different levels, such as by wealth or social class
Breton a native of Brittany, a region of France
bewildering extremely confusing
antechambers small rooms leading into larger rooms
tapestry a heavy cloth, often with designs woven in, usually hung on walls
coquettish having to do with flirting
intimate close

When she sat down to dinner, before the round table covered with a tablecloth used for three days, opposite her husband, who uncovered the soup **tureen** and declared with a delighted air, "Ah, the good soup! I don't know anything better than that," she thought of dainty dinners, of shining silverware, of tapestry that peopled the walls with ancient personages and with strange birds flying in the midst of a fairy forest; and she thought of delicious dishes served on marvelous plates and of the whispered **gallantries** to which you listen with a **sphinx-like** smile while you are eating the pink meat of a trout or the wings of a quail.

She had no gowns, no jewels, nothing. And she loved nothing but that. She felt made for that. She would have liked so much to please, to be envied, to be charming, to be sought after.

She had a friend, a former schoolmate at the convent, who was rich, and whom she did not like to go to see any more because she felt so sad when she came home.

But one evening her husband came home with a triumphant air and holding a large envelope in his hand.

"There," said he, "there is something for you."

....

tureen a large bowl
gallantries courteous and flattering words
sphinx-like mysterious (like the Sphinx, the creature from Greek mythology noted for asking a challenging riddle)

She tore the paper quickly and drew out a printed card which bore these words:

> *The Minister of Education and Madame Georges Ramponneau request the honor of* **M. and Mme.** *Loisel's company at the palace of the Ministry on Monday evening, January 18th.*

Instead of being delighted, as her husband had hoped, she threw the invitation on the table crossly, muttering, "What do you want me to do with that?"

"But, my dear, I thought you would be pleased. You never go out, and this is such a fine opportunity. I had great trouble to get it. Everyone wants to go; it is very select, and they are not giving many invitations to clerks. The whole official world will be there."

She looked at him with an irritated glance and said impatiently, "And what do you wish me to put on my back?"

He had not thought of that. He stammered, "Why, the gown you go to the theatre in. It looks very well to me."

He stopped, distracted, seeing that his wife was weeping. Two great tears ran slowly from the corners of her eyes toward the corners of her mouth.

"What's the matter? What's the matter?" he stuttered.

M. and Mme. Monsieur (Mister) and Madame (Mrs.)

By a violent effort she conquered her grief and replied in a calm voice, while she wiped her wet cheeks, "Nothing. Only I have no gown, and, therefore I can't go to this ball. Give your card to some colleague whose wife is better equipped than I am."

He was in despair. He resumed, "See here, Mathilde. How much would it cost, a suitable gown, which you could use on other occasions—something very simple?"

She reflected several seconds, making her calculations and wondering also what sum she could ask without drawing on herself an immediate refusal and a frightened exclamation from the economical clerk.

Finally she replied, with hesitation, "I don't know exactly, but I think I could manage it with four hundred **francs**."

He grew a little pale, because he was setting aside just that amount to buy a gun and treat himself to a little shooting next summer on the plain of Nanterre, with several friends who went to shoot larks there on Sundays.

But he said, "Very well. I will give you four hundred francs. And try to have a pretty gown."

The day of the ball drew near and Madame Loisel seemed sad, restless, anxious. Her gown was ready, however.

....

francs French money

Her husband said to her one evening, "What is the matter? Come, you have seemed very odd these last three days."

And she answered, "It annoys me not to have a single piece of jewelry, not a single ornament, nothing to put on. I shall look poverty-stricken. I would almost rather not go at all."

"You might wear natural flowers," said her husband. "They're very stylish at this time of year. For ten francs you can get two or three magnificent roses."

She was not convinced. "No; there's nothing more **humiliating** than to look poor among other women who are rich."

"How silly you are!" her husband cried. "Go look up your friend, Madame Forestier, and ask her to lend you some jewels. You know her quite well enough to do that."

She gave a cry of joy: "True! I never thought of it."

The next day she went to her friend and told her of her distress.

Madame Forestier went to a wardrobe with a mirror, took out a large jewel box, brought it back, opened it and said to Madame Loisel, "Choose, my dear."

She saw first some bracelets, then a pearl necklace, then a Venetian gold cross set with precious stones, of admirable workmanship. She tried on the ornaments before the mirror, hesitated, and could not make up her mind to part

---

humiliating humbling; extremely embarrassing

with them, to give them back. She kept asking, "Haven't you any more?"

"Why, yes. Look further; I don't know what you like."

Suddenly she discovered, in a black satin box, a superb diamond necklace, and her heart throbbed with an **immoderate** desire. Her hands trembled as she took it. She fastened it round her throat, outside her high-necked waist, and was lost in ecstasy at her reflection in the mirror.

Then she asked, hesitating, filled with anxious doubt, "Will you lend me this, only this?"

"Why, yes, certainly."

She threw her arms round her friend's neck, kissed her with great emotion, then fled with her treasure.

The night of the ball arrived. Madame Loisel was a great success. She was prettier than any other woman there, elegant, graceful, smiling, and wild with joy. All the men looked at her, asked her name, sought to be introduced. All the officials of the Cabinet wished to waltz with her. She was noticed by the minister himself.

She danced with **rapture**, with passion, **intoxicated** by pleasure, forgetting all in the triumph of her beauty, in the glory of her success, in a sort of cloud of happiness made up of all this admiration, of all these awakened desires, and of this victory so complete and so sweet to a woman's heart.

....

immoderate excessive; extreme
rapture ecstasy; great happiness
intoxicated wildly excited

She left the ball about four o'clock in the morning. Her husband had been sleeping since midnight in a little deserted **anteroom** with three other gentlemen whose wives were enjoying the ball.

He threw over her shoulders the wraps he had brought, the modest wraps of common life, the poverty of which contrasted with the elegance of the ball dress. She felt this and wished to escape so as not to be noticed by the other women, who were enveloping themselves in costly furs.

Loisel held her back, saying, "Wait a bit. You will catch cold outside. I will call a cab."

But she did not listen to him and rapidly descended the stairs. When they reached the street, they could not find a carriage and began to look for one, shouting after the cabmen passing at a distance.

They went toward the Seine in despair, shivering with cold. At last they found on the **quay** one of those ancient night cabs which, as though they were ashamed to show their shabbiness during the day, are never seen round Paris until after dark.

It took them to their dwelling in the Rue des Martyrs, and sadly they mounted the stairs to their flat. All was ended for her. As to him, he reflected that he must be at the ministry at ten o'clock that morning.

....

anteroom a waiting room
quay a riverside area where ships may dock

She removed her wraps before the glass so as to see herself once more in all her glory. But suddenly she uttered a cry. She no longer had the necklace around her neck!

"What is the matter with you?" demanded her husband, already half undressed.

She turned distractedly toward him. "I have—I have—I've lost Madame Forestier's necklace," she cried.

He stood up, bewildered. "What!—how? Impossible!"

They looked among the folds of her skirt, of her cloak, in her pockets, everywhere, but did not find it.

"You're sure you had it on when you left the ball?" he asked. "Yes, I felt it in the vestibule of the palace."

"But if you had lost it in the street we should have heard it fall. It must be in the cab."

"Yes, probably. Did you take his number?"

"No. And you—didn't you notice it?"

"No."

They looked at each other, **thunderstruck**. At last Loisel put on his clothes.

"I shall go back on foot," said he, "over the whole route, to see whether I can find it."

He went out. She sat waiting on a chair in her ball dress, without strength to go to bed, overwhelmed, without any fire, without a thought.

Her husband returned about seven o'clock. He had found nothing.

....

thunderstruck shocked; amazed

He went to police headquarters, to the newspaper offices to offer a reward; he went to the cab companies—everywhere he was urged by the least spark of hope.

She waited all day, in the same condition of mad fear before this terrible calamity.

Loisel returned at night with a hollow, pale face. He had discovered nothing.

"You must write to your friend," said he, "that you have broken the clasp of her necklace and that you are having it mended. That will give us time to turn round."

She wrote as he dictated.

At the end of a week they had lost all hope. Loisel, who had aged five years, declared, "We must consider how to replace those jewels."

The next day they took the case and went to the jeweler whose name was in the cover. He consulted his books.

"It was not I, madame, who sold that necklace; I must simply have furnished the case."

Then they went from jeweler to jeweler, searching for a necklace like the other, trying to recall it, both sick with grief and anxiety.

They found, in a shop at the Palais Royal, a string of diamonds that seemed to them exactly like the one they had lost. It was worth forty thousand francs. They could have it for thirty-six.

So they begged the jeweler not to sell it for three days yet. And they made a bargain that he should buy it back for thirty-four thousand francs, in case they should find the lost necklace before the end of February.

Loisel possessed eighteen thousand francs that his father had left him. He would borrow the rest.

He did borrow, asking a thousand francs of one, five hundred of another, five **louis** here, three louis there. He gave notes, took up ruinous obligations, dealt with **usurers** and all manner of lenders. He compromised all the rest of his life, risked signing a note without even knowing whether he could meet it; and, frightened by the trouble yet to come, by the black misery that was about to fall upon him, by the prospect of all the physical privations and moral tortures that he was to suffer, he went to get the new necklace, laying upon the jeweler's counter thirty-six thousand francs.

When Madame Loisel took back the necklace Madame Forestier said to her with a chilly manner, "You should have returned it sooner; I might have needed it."

She did not open the case, as her friend had so much feared. If she had detected the substitution, what would she have thought, what would she have said? Would she not have taken Madame Loisel for a thief?

----

louis French money
usurers people who lend money at excessive interest rates

Thereafter Madame Loisel knew the horrible existence of the needy. She bore her part, however, with sudden heroism. That dreadful debt must be paid. She would pay it. They dismissed their servant; they changed their lodgings; they rented a garret under the roof.

She came to know what heavy housework meant and the **odious** cares of the kitchen. She washed the dishes, using her dainty fingers and rosy nails on greasy pots and pans. She washed the soiled linen, the shirts and the dishcloths, which she dried upon a line; she carried the garbage down to the street every morning and carried up the water, stopping for breath at every landing. And, dressed like a woman of the people, she went to the fruit seller, the grocer, the butcher, a basket on her arm, bargaining, meeting with insults, defending her miserable money, sou by sou.

Every month they had to pay off some notes, renew others, obtain more time.

Her husband worked evenings, keeping a tradesman's accounts, and late at night he often copied manuscript for five sous a page.

This life lasted ten years.

At the end of ten years they had paid everything, everything, with the rates of usury and the accumulations of the compound interest.

....

odious hateful; terrible

Madame Loisel looked old now. She had become the woman of **impoverished** households—strong and hard and rough. With frowsy hair, skirts askew, and red hands, she talked loud while washing the floor with great swishes of water. But sometimes, when her husband was at the office, she sat down near the window and she thought of that happy evening long ago, of that ball where she had been so beautiful and so admired.

What would have happened if she had not lost that necklace? Who knows? Who knows? How strange and changeful is life! How small a thing is needed to make or ruin us!

But one Sunday, having gone to take a walk in the Champs Elysees to refresh herself after the labors of the week, she suddenly perceived a woman who was leading a child. It was Madame Forestier, still young, still beautiful, still charming.

Madame Loisel felt moved. Should she speak to her? Yes, certainly. And now that she had paid, she would tell her all about it. Why not?

She went up.

"Good-day, Jeanne."

The other, astonished to be greeted familiarly by this woman of the people, did not recognize her at all and stammered, "But—madame!—I do not know—You must be mistaken."

---

impoverished made poor; reduced to poverty

"No. I am Mathilde Loisel."

Her friend uttered a cry. "Oh, my poor Mathilde! How you are changed!"

"Yes, I have had a hard life since I last saw you, and great poverty—and that because of you!"

"Of me! How so?"

"Do you remember that diamond necklace you lent me to wear at the ministerial ball?"

"Yes. Well?"

"Well, I lost it."

"What do you mean? You brought it back."

"I brought you back another exactly like it. And it has taken us ten years to pay for it. You can understand that it was not easy for us, for us who had nothing. At last it is ended, and I am very glad."

Madame Forestier had stopped.

"You say that you bought a necklace of diamonds to replace mine?"

"Yes. You never noticed it, then! They were very similar." And she smiled with proud and **naive** joy.

Madame Forestier, deeply moved, took her hands.

"Oh, my poor Mathilde! Why, my necklace was **paste**! It was worth at most only five hundred francs!" ❖

....

naive simple; lacking sophistication
paste a shiny kind of glass used to make artificial gems

R.M.S *Titanic*

by Hanson W. Baldwin

The R.M.S. Titanic *was a giant luxury cruise ship that left Southampton, England, to sail to New York in April 1912. The ship hit an iceberg and sunk. Around 1,500 people died. The following article from 1934 describes the tragedy. The author researched ship's logs, interviews, and other records to write the article.*

I

The White Star liner *Titanic*, largest ship the world had ever known, sailed from Southampton on her **maiden** voyage to New York on April 10, 1912. The paint on her strakes was fair and bright; she was fresh from Harland and Wolff's Belfast yards, strong in the strength of her forty-six thousand tons of steel, bent, hammered, shaped, and riveted through the three years of her slow birth.

There was little fuss and fanfare at her sailing; her sister ship, the *Olympic*—slightly smaller than the *Titanic*—had been in service for some months and to her had gone the thunder of the cheers.

But the *Titanic* needed no whistling steamers or shouting crowds to call attention to her **superlative** qualities. Her bulk dwarfed the ships near her as longshoremen singled up her mooring lines and cast off the turns of heavy rope from the dock bollards. She was not only the largest ship afloat, but was believed to be the safest. Carlisle, her builder, had given her double bottoms and had divided her hull into sixteen watertight compartments, which made her, men thought, unsinkable. She had been built to be and had been described as a gigantic lifeboat. Her designers' dreams of a triplescrew giant, a luxurious, floating hotel, which could speed to New York at twenty-three knots, had

....

maiden first
superlative excellent; magnificent

been carefully translated from blueprints and mold loft lines at the Belfast yards into a living reality.

The *Titanic's* sailing from Southampton, though quiet, was not wholly uneventful. As the liner moved slowly toward the end of her dock that April day, the surge of her passing sucked away from the quay the steamer *New York*, moored just to seaward of the *Titanic's* berth. There were sharp cracks as the manila mooring lines of the *New York* parted under the strain. The frayed ropes writhed and whistled through the air and snapped down among the waving crowd on the pier; the *New York* swung toward the *Titanic's* bow, was checked and dragged back to the dock barely in time to avert a collision. Seamen muttered, thought it an **ominous** start.

Past Spithead and the Isle of Wight the *Titanic* steamed. She called at Cherbourg at dusk and then laid her course for Queenstown. At 1:30 p.m. on Thursday, April 11, she stood out of Queenstown harbor, screaming gulls soaring in her wake, with 2,201 persons—men, women, and children—aboard.

Occupying the Empire bedrooms and Georgian suites of the first-class accommodations were many well-known men and women—Colonel John Jacob Astor and his young bride; Major Archibald Butt, military aide to President Taft, and his friend Frank D. Millet, the painter; John B. Thayer, vice president of the Pennsylvania Railroad, and Charles

....

ominous foreboding; threatening; suggestive of bad things to come

M. Hays, president of the Grand Trunk Railway of Canada; W. T. Stead, the English journalist; Jacques Futrelle, French novelist; H. B. Harris, theatrical manager, and Mrs. Harris; Mr. and Mrs. Isidor Straus; and J. Bruce Ismay, chairman and managing director of the White Star Line.

Down in the plain wooden cabins of the **steerage class** were 706 immigrants to the land of promise, and trimly stowed in the great holds was a cargo valued at $420,000: oak beams, sponges, wine, calabashes, and an odd miscellany of the common and the rare.

The *Titanic* took her departure on Fastnet Light and, heading into the night, laid her course for New York. She was due at quarantine the following Wednesday morning.

Sunday dawned fair and clear. The *Titanic* steamed smoothly toward the west, faint streamers of brownish smoke trailing from her funnels. The **purser** held services in the saloon in the morning; on the steerage deck aft the immigrants were playing games and a Scotsman was puffing "The Campbells Are Coming" on his bagpipes in the midst of the uproar.

At 9:00 a.m. a message from the steamer *Caronia* sputtered into the wireless shack:

> Captain, *Titanic*—Westbound steamers report bergs growlers and field ice 42 degrees N. from 49 degrees to 51 degrees W. 12th April.
>
> Compliments—Barr.

steerage class cabins below deck which were crowded, dark, and often dirty
purser an ship's employee who took care of the passengers

It was cold in the afternoon; the sun was brilliant, but the *Titanic*, her **screws** turning over at seventy-five revolutions per minute, was approaching the Banks.

In the Marconi cabin Second Operator Harold Bride, earphones clamped on his head, was figuring accounts; he did not stop to answer when he heard MWL, Continental Morse for the nearby Leyland liner, *Californian*, calling the *Titanic*. The *Californian* had some message about three icebergs; he didn't bother then to take it down. About 1:42 p.m. the **rasping spark** of those days spoke again across the water. It was the *Baltic*, calling the *Titanic*, warning her of ice on the steamer track. Bride took the message down and sent it up to the bridge. The officer-of-the-deck glanced at it; sent it to the bearded master of the *Titanic*, Captain E. C. Smith, a veteran of the White Star service. It was lunchtime then; the captain, walking along the promenade deck, saw Mr. Ismay, stopped, and handed him the message without comment. Ismay read it, stuffed it in his pocket, told two ladies about the icebergs, and resumed his walk. Later, about 7:15 p.m., the captain requested the return of the message in order to post it in the chart room for the information of officers.

Dinner that night in the Jacobean dining room was gay. It was **bitter** on deck, but the night was calm and fine; the sky was moonless but studded with stars twinkling coldly in the clear air.

....

screws propellers
rasping spark message received in Morse code
bitter very cold

After dinner some of the second-class passengers gathered in the saloon, where the Reverend Mr. Carter conducted a "hymn singsong." It was almost ten o'clock and the stewards were waiting with biscuits and coffee as the group sang:

O, hear us when we cry to Thee
For those in peril on the sea.

On the bridge Second Officer Lightoller—short, stocky, efficient—was relieved at ten o'clock by First Officer Murdoch. Lightoller had talked with other officers about the **proximity** of ice; at least five wireless ice warnings had reached the ship; lookouts had been cautioned to be alert; captains and officers expected to reach the field at any time after 9:30 p.m. At twenty-two knots, its speed **unslackened**, the *Titanic* plowed on through the night.

Lightoller left the darkened bridge to his **relief** and turned in. Captain Smith went to his cabin. The steerage was long since quiet; in the first and second cabins' lights were going out; voices were growing still; people were asleep. Murdoch paced back and forth on the bridge, peering out over the dark water, glancing now and then at the compass in front of Quartermaster Hichens at the wheel.

In the crow's-nest, lookout Frederick Fleet and his partner, Leigh, gazed down at the water, still and unruffled in the dim, starlit darkness. Behind and below them the

proximity nearness
unslackened not made slower
relief a replacement

ship, a white shadow with here and there a last winking
light; ahead of them a dark and silent and cold ocean.

There was a sudden clang. "Dong-dong. Dong-dong.
Dong-dong. Dong!" The metal clapper of the great ship's
bell struck out 11:30. Mindful of the warnings, Fleet
strained his eyes, searching the darkness for the dreaded
ice. But there were only the stars and the sea.

In the wireless room, where Phillips, first operator,
had relieved Bride, the buzz of the *Californian's* set again
crackled into the earphones:

> *Californian*: "Say, old man, we are stuck here,
> surrounded by ice."
>
> *Titanic*: "Shut up, shut up; keep out. I am talking to
> Cape Race; you are jamming my signals."

Then, a few minutes later—about 11:40 . . .

II

Out of the dark she came, a vast, dim, white, monstrous shape, directly in the *Titanic's* path. For a moment Fleet doubted his eyes. But she was a deadly reality, this **ghastly** thing. Frantically, Fleet struck three bells—something dead ahead. He snatched the telephone and called the bridge:

"Iceberg! Right ahead!"

The first officer heard but did not stop to acknowledge the message.

"Hard-a-starboard!"

Hichens strained at the wheel; the bow swung slowly to port. The monster was almost upon them now.

Murdoch leaped to the engine-room telegraph. Bells clanged. Far below in the engine room those bells struck the first warning. Danger! The indicators on the dial faces swung round to "Stop!" Then "Full speed astern!" Frantically the engineers turned great valve wheels; answered the bridge bells…

There was a slight shock, a brief scraping, a small list to port. Shell ice—slabs and chunks of it—fell on the foredeck. Slowly the *Titanic* stopped.

Captain Smith hurried out of his cabin.

"What has the ship struck?"

Murdoch answered, "An iceberg, sir. I hard-a-starboarded and reversed the engines, and I was going to hard-a-port

---

ghastly terrifying

around it, but she was too close. I could not do any more. I have closed the watertight doors."

Fourth Officer Boxhall, other officers, the carpenter, came to the bridge. The captain sent Boxhall and the carpenter below to ascertain the damage.

A few lights switched on in the first and second cabins; sleepy passengers peered through porthole glass; some casually asked the stewards:

"Why have we stopped?"

"I don't know, sir, but I don't suppose it is anything much."

In the smoking room a **quorum** of gamblers and their prey were still sitting round a poker table; the usual crowd of kibitzers looked on. They had felt the slight jar of the collision and had seen an eighty-foot ice mountain glide by the smoking-room windows, but the night was calm and clear, the *Titanic* was "unsinkable"; they hadn't bothered to go on deck.

But far below, in the warren of passages on the starboard side forward, in the forward holds and boiler rooms, men could see that the *Titanic*'s hurt was mortal. In No. 6 boiler room, where the red glow from the furnaces lighted up the naked, sweaty chests of coal-blackened firemen, water was pouring through a great gash about two feet above the floor plates. This was no slow leak; the ship was open to the sea; in ten minutes there were eight feet of water in No. 6. Long

---

quorum a group or a minimum number of people required for some event or activity

before then the stokers had raked the flaming fires out of the furnaces and had scrambled through the watertight doors in No. 5 or had climbed up the long steel ladders to safety. When Boxhall looked at the mailroom in No. 3 hold, twenty-four feet above the keel, the mailbags were already floating about in the slushing water. In No. 5 boiler room a stream of water spurted into an empty bunker. All six compartments forward of No. 4 were open to the sea; in ten seconds the iceberg's jagged claw had ripped a three-hundred-foot slash in the bottom of the great *Titanic*.

Reports came to the bridge; Ismay in dressing gown ran out on deck in the cold, still, starlit night, climbed up the bridge ladder.

"What has happened?"

Captain Smith: "We have struck ice."

"Do you think she is seriously damaged?"

Captain Smith: "I'm afraid she is."

Ismay went below and passed Chief Engineer William Bell, fresh from an inspection of the damaged compartments. Bell **corroborated** the captain's statement; hurried back down the glistening steel ladders to his duty. Man after man followed him—Thomas Andrews, one of the ship's designers, Archie Frost, the builder's chief engineer, and his twenty assistants—men who had no posts of duty in the engine room but whose traditions called them there.

....

corroborated agreed with, supported

On deck, in corridor and stateroom, life flowed again. Men, women, and children awoke and questioned; orders were given to uncover the lifeboats; water rose into the firemen's quarters; half-dressed stokers streamed up on deck. But the passengers—most of them—did not know that the *Titanic* was sinking. The shock of the collision had been so slight that some were not awakened by it; the *Titanic* was so huge that she must be unsinkable; the night was too calm, too beautiful, to think of death at sea.

Captain Smith half ran to the door of the radio shack. Bride, partly dressed, eyes dulled with sleep, was standing behind Phillips, waiting.

"Send the call for assistance."

The blue spark danced: "CQD—CQD—CQD—CQ—"

Miles away Marconi men heard. Cape Race heard it, and the steamships *La Provence* and *Mt. Temple*.

The sea was surging into the *Titanic*'s hold. At 12:20 the water burst into the seamen's quarters through a collapsed fore-and-aft wooden bulkhead. Pumps strained in the engine rooms—men and machinery making a **futile** fight against the sea. Steadily the water rose.

The boats were swung out—slowly, for the deckhands were late in reaching their stations; there had been no boat drill, and many of the crew did not know to what boats they were assigned. Orders were shouted; the safety valves

---

futile useless

had lifted, and steam was blowing off in a great rushing roar. In the chart house Fourth Officer Boxhall bent above a chart, working rapidly with pencil and dividers.

12:25 a.m. Boxhall's position is sent out to a fleet of vessels: "Come at once; we have struck a berg."

To the Cunarder *Carpathia* (Arthur Henry Rostron, Master, New York to Liverpool, fifty-eight miles away): "It's a CQD, old man. Position 41–46N.; 50–14 W."

The blue spark dancing: "Sinking; cannot hear for noise of steam."

12:30 a.m. The word is passed: "Women and children in the boats." Stewards finish waking their passengers below; life preservers are tied on; some men smile at the precaution. "The *Titanic* is unsinkable." The *Mt. Temple* starts for the *Titanic*; the *Carpathia*, with a double watch in her stokeholds, radios, "Coming hard." The CQD changes the course of many ships—but not of one; the operator of the *Californian*, nearby, has just put down his earphones and turned in.

The CQD flashes over land and sea from Cape Race to New York; newspaper city rooms leap to life and presses whir.

On the *Titanic*, water creeps over the bulkhead between Nos. 5 and 6 firerooms. She is going down by the head; the engineers—fighting a losing battle—are forced back foot by foot by the rising water. Down the **promenade** deck, Happy Jock Hume, the bandsman, runs with his instrument.

12:45 a.m. Murdoch, in charge on the starboard side, eyes tragic, but calm and cool, orders boat No. 7 lowered. The women hang back; they want no boat ride on an ice-strewn sea; the *Titanic* is unsinkable. The men encourage them, explain that this is just a precautionary measure: "We'll see you again at breakfast." There is little confusion; passengers stream slowly to the boat deck. In the steerage the immigrants chatter excitedly.

A sudden sharp hiss—a streaked flare against the night; Boxhall sends a rocket toward the sky. It explodes, and a parachute of white stars lights up the icy sea. "God! Rockets!" The band plays ragtime.

No. 8 is lowered, and No. 5. Ismay, still in dressing gown, calls for women and children, handles lines, stumbles in the way of an officer, is told to "get the hell out of here." Third Officer Pitman takes charge of No. 5; as he swings into the boat, Murdoch grasps his hand. "Goodbye and good luck, old man."

No. 6 goes over the side. There are only twenty-eight people in a lifeboat with a capacity of sixty-five.

A light stabs from the bridge; Boxhall is calling in Morse flashes, again and again, to a strange ship stopped in the ice jam five to ten miles away. Another rocket drops

---

promenade deck upper deck where passengers stroll

its shower of sparks above the ice-strewn sea and the dying ship.

1:00 a.m. Slowly the water creeps higher; the fore ports of the *Titanic* are dipping into the sea. Rope squeaks through blocks; lifeboats drop jerkily seaward. Through the shouting on the decks comes the sound of the band playing ragtime.

The "Millionaires' Special" leaves the ship—boat No. 1, with a capacity of forty people, carries only Sir Cosmo and Lady Duff Gordon and ten others. Aft, the frightened immigrants mill and jostle and rush for a boat. An officer's fist flies out; three shots are fired in the air, and the panic is **quelled** ....Four Chinese sneak unseen into a boat and hide in the bottom.

1:20 a.m. Water is coming into No. 4 boiler room. Stokers slice and shovel as water laps about their ankles— steam for the **dynamos**, steam for the dancing spark! As the water rises, great ash hoes rake the flaming coals from the furnaces. Safety valves pop; the stokers retreat aft, and the watertight doors clang shut behind them.

The rockets fling their splendor toward the stars. The boats are more heavily loaded now, for the passengers know the *Titanic* is sinking. Women cling and sob. The great screws aft are rising clear of the sea. Half-filled boats

quelled subdued; put to an end
dynamos furnaces that power the engines

are ordered to come alongside the cargo ports and take on more passengers, but the ports are never opened—and the boats are never filled. Others pull for the steamer's light miles away but never reach it; the lights disappear; the unknown ship steams off.

The water rises and the band plays ragtime.

1:30 a.m. Lightoller is getting the port boats off; Murdoch, the starboard. As one boat is lowered into the sea, a boat officer fires his gun along the ship's side to stop a rush from the lower decks. A woman tries to take her Great Dane into a boat with her; she is refused and steps out of the boat to die with her dog. Millet's "little smile which played on his lips all through the voyage" plays no more; his lips are grim, but he waves goodbye and brings wraps for the women.

Benjamin Guggenheim, in evening clothes, smiles and says, "We've dressed up in our best and are prepared to go down like gentlemen."

1:40 a.m. Boat 14 is clear, and then 13, 16, 15, and C. The lights still shine, but the *Baltic* hears the blue spark say, "Engine room getting flooded."

The *Olympia* signals, "Am lighting up all possible boilers as fast as can."

Major Butt helps women into the last boats and waves goodbye to them. Mrs. Straus puts her foot on the gunwale of a lifeboat; then she draws back and goes to her husband: "We have been together many years; where you go, I will go." Colonel John Jacob Astor puts his young wife in a lifeboat, steps back, taps cigarette on fingernail: "Goodbye, dearie; I'll join you later."

1:45 a.m. The foredeck is under water; the fo'c'sle head almost awash; the great stern is lifted high toward the bright stars; and still the band plays. Mr. and Mrs. Harris approach a lifeboat arm in arm.

Officer: "Ladies first, please."

Harris bows, smiles, steps back: "Of course, certainly; ladies first."

Boxhall fires the last rocket, then leaves in charge of boat No. 2.

2:00 a.m. She is dying now; her bow goes deeper, her stern higher. But there must be steam. Below in the stokeholds the sweaty firemen keep steam up for the flaring lights and the dancing spark. The glowing coals slide and tumble over the slanted grate bars; the sea pounds behind that yielding bulkhead. But the spark dances on.

The *Asian* hears Phillips try the new signal—SOS.

Boat No. 4 has left now; boat D leaves ten minutes later. Jacques Futrelle clasps his wife: "For God's sake, go! It's your last chance; go!" Madame Futrelle is half forced into the boat. It clears the side.

There are about 660 people in the boats and 1,500 still on the sinking *Titanic*. On top of the officers' quarters, men work frantically to get the two collapsibles stowed there over the side. Water is over the forward part of

A deck now; it surges up the companionways toward the boat deck. In the radio shack, Bride has slipped a coat and life jacket about Phillips as the first operator sits hunched over his key, sending—still sending—"41–46 N.; 50–14 W. CQD—CQD—SOS—SOS—"

The captain's tired white face appears at the radio-room door. "Men, you have done your full duty. You can do no more. Now, it's every man for himself." The captain disappears—back to his sinking bridge, where Painter, his personal steward, stands quietly waiting for orders. The spark dances on. Bride turns his back and goes into the inner cabin. As he does so, a stoker, grimed with coal, mad with fear, steals into the shack and reaches for the life jacket on Phillips's back. Bride wheels about and brains him with a wrench.

2:10 a.m. Below decks the steam is still holding, though the pressure is falling—rapidly. In the gymnasium on the boat deck, the athletic instructor watches quietly as two gentlemen ride the bicycles and another swings casually at the punching bag. Mail clerks stagger up the boat-deck stairways, dragging soaked mail sacks. The spark still dances. The band still plays—but not ragtime:

Nearer my God to Thee.

Nearer to Thee ...

A few men take up the refrain; others kneel on the slanting decks to pray. Many run and scramble aft, where hundreds are clinging above the silent screws on the great uptilted **stern**. The spark still dances and the lights still flare; the engineers are on the job. The hymn comes to its close. Bandmaster Hartley, Yorkshireman violinist, taps his bow against a bulkhead, calls for "Autumn" as the water curls about his feet, and the eight musicians brace themselves against the ship's slant. People are leaping from the decks into the nearby water—the icy water. A woman cries, "Oh, save me, save me!" A man answers, "Good lady, save yourself. Only God can save you now." The band plays "Autumn":

> God of Mercy and Compassion!
>
> Look with pity on my pain ...

The water creeps over the bridge where the *Titanic's* master stands; heavily he steps out to meet it.

2:17 a.m. "CQ—" The *Virginian* hears a ragged, blurred CQ, then an abrupt stop. The blue spark dances no more. The lights flicker out; the engineers have lost their battle.

2:18 a.m. Men run about blackened decks; leap into the night; are swept into the sea by the curling wave that licks up the *Titanic's* length. Lightoller does not leave the ship; the ship leaves him; there are hundreds like him, but only a few who live to tell of it. The **funnels** still swim above the water, but the ship is climbing to the **perpendicular**; the bridge is under and most of the foremast; the great

....

stern back end of a ship
funnels smokestacks
perpendicular at a ninety degree angle

stern rises like a squat leviathan. Men swim away from the sinking ship; others drop from the stern.

The band plays in the darkness, the water lapping upward:

> Hold me up in mighty waters,
>
> Keep my eyes on things above,
>
> Righteousness, divine atonement, Peace and everlas…

The forward funnel snaps and crashes into the sea; its steel tons hammer out of existence swimmers struggling in the freezing water. Streams of sparks, of smoke and steam, burst from the after funnels. The ship upends to 50—to 60 degrees.

Down in the black **abyss** of the stokeholds, of the engine rooms, where the dynamos have whirred at long last to a stop, the stokers and the engineers are reeling against the hot metal, the rising water clutching at their knees. The boilers, the engine cylinders, rip from their bed plates; crash through bulkheads; rumble—steel against steel.

The *Titanic* stands on end, poised briefly for the plunge. Slowly she slides to her grave—slowly at first, and then more quickly—quickly—quickly.

2:20 a.m. The greatest ship in the world has sunk. From the calm, dark waters, where the floating lifeboats move, there goes up, in the white wake of her passing, "one long continuous moan."

....

abyss a deep, seemingly endless hole or pit

III

The boats that the *Titanic* had launched pulled safely away
from the slight suction of the sinking ship, pulled away
from the screams that came from the lips of the freezing
men and women in the water. The boats were poorly
manned and badly equipped, and they had been unevenly
loaded. Some carried so few seamen that women bent to
the oars. Mrs. Astor tugged at an oar handle; the Countess
of Rothes took a tiller. Shivering stokers in sweaty, coal-
blackened singlets and light trousers steered in some boats;
stewards in white coats rowed in others. Ismay was in the
last boat that left the ship from the starboard side; with
Mr. Carter of Philadelphia and two seamen he tugged at
the oars. In one of the lifeboats an Italian with a broken
wrist—disguised in a woman's shawl and hat—huddled
on the floorboards, ashamed now that fear had left him.
In another rode the only baggage saved from the *Titanic*—
the carryall of Samuel L. Goldenberg, one of the rescued
passengers.

There were only a few boats that were heavily loaded;
most of those that were half-empty made but **perfunctory**
efforts to pick up the moaning swimmers, their officers and
crew fearing they would endanger the living if they pulled
back into the midst of the dying. Some boats beat off the
freezing victims; fear-crazed men and women struck with

---

perfunctory with little effort

oars at the heads of swimmers. One woman drove her fist into the face of a half-dead man as he tried feebly to climb over the gunwale. Two other women helped him in and staunched the flow of blood from the ring cuts on his face.

One of the collapsible boats, which had floated off the top of the officers' quarters when the *Titanic* sank, was an icy haven for thirty or forty men. The boat had capsized as the ship sank; men swam to it, clung to it, climbed upon its slippery bottom, stood knee-deep in water in the freezing air. Chunks of ice swirled about their legs; their soaked clothing clutched their bodies in icy folds. Colonel Archibald Gracie was cast up there, Gracie who had leaped from the stern as the *Titanic* sank; young Thayer who had seen his father die; Lightoller who had twice been sucked down with the ship and twice blown to the surface by

a belch of air; Bride, the second operator; and Phillips, the first. There were many stokers, half-naked; it was a shivering company. They stood there in the icy sea, under the far stars, and sang and prayed—the Lord's Prayer. After a while a lifeboat came and picked them off, but Phillips was dead then or died soon afterward in the boat.

Only a few of the boats had lights; only one—No. 2— had a light that was of any use to the *Carpathia*, twisting through the ice field to the rescue. Other ships were "coming hard" too; one, the *Californian*, was still dead to opportunity.

The blue sparks still danced, but not the *Titanic's*. *La Provence* to *Celtic*: "Nobody has heard the *Titanic* for about two hours."

It was 2:40 when the *Carpathia* first sighted the green light from No. 2 boat; it was 4:10 when she picked up the first boat and learned that the *Titanic* had **foundered**. The last of the moaning cries had just died away then.

Captain Rostron took the survivors aboard, boatload by boatload. He was ready for them, but only a small minority of them required much medical attention. Bride's feet were twisted and frozen; others were suffering from exposure; one died, and seven were dead when taken from the boats, and were buried at sea.

It was then that the fleet of racing ships learned they were too late; the *Parisian* heard the weak signals of MPA, the *Carpathia*, report the death of the *Titanic*. It was

....

foundered filled with water and sank

then—or soon afterward, when her radio operator put on his earphones—that the *Californian*, the ship that had been within sight as the *Titanic* was sinking, first learned of the disaster.

And it was then, in all its white-green majesty, that the *Titanic's* survivors saw the iceberg, tinted with the sunrise, floating idly, pack ice jammed about its base, other bergs heaving slowly nearby on the blue breast of the sea.

IV

But it was not until later that the world knew, for wireless then was not what wireless is today, and **garbled** messages had nourished a hope that all of the *Titanic's* company were safe. Not until Monday evening, when P. A. S. Franklin, vice president of the International Mercantile Marine Company, received relayed messages in New York that left little hope, did the full extent of the disaster begin to be known. Partial and garbled lists of the survivors; rumors of heroism and cowardice; stories spun out of newspaper imagination, based on a few bare facts and many false reports, misled the world, terrified and frightened it. It was not until Thursday night, when the *Carpathia* steamed into the North River, that the full truth was pieced together.

Flashlights flared on the black river when the *Carpathia* stood up to her dock. Tugs nosed about her, shunted her toward Pier 54. Thirty thousand people jammed the streets;

garbled confused

ambulances and stretchers stood on the pier; coroners and physicians waited.

In midstream the Cunarder dropped over the *Titanic's* lifeboats; then she headed toward the dock. Beneath the customs letters on the pier stood relatives of the 711 survivors, relatives of the missing—hoping against hope. The *Carpathia* cast her lines ashore; **stevedores** looped them over bollards. The dense throngs stood quiet as the first survivor stepped down the gangway. The woman half-staggered—led by customs guards—beneath her letter. A "low wailing" moan came from the crowd; fell, grew in volume, and dropped again.

Thus ended the maiden voyage of the *Titanic*. The lifeboats brought to New York by the *Carpathia*, a few deck chairs and gratings awash in the ice field off the Grand Bank eight hundred miles from shore, were all that was left of the world's greatest ship.

V

The aftermath of weeping and regret, of **recriminations** and investigations, dragged on for weeks. Charges and countercharges were hurled about; the White Star Line was bitterly criticized; Ismay was denounced on the floor of the Senate as a coward but was defended by those who had been with him on the sinking *Titanic* and by the Board of Trade investigation in England.

....

stevedores people who help dock, load, and unload a boat
recriminations criticisms or accusations

It was not until weeks later, when the hastily convened Senate investigation in the United States and the Board of Trade report in England had been completed, that the whole story was told. The Senate investigating committee, under the chairmanship of Senator Smith, who was attacked in both the American and the British press as a "backwoods politician," brought out numerous pertinent facts, though its proceedings verged at times on the **farcical**. Senator Smith was ridiculed for his lack of knowledge of the sea when he asked witnesses, "Of what is an iceberg composed?" and "Did any of the passengers take refuge in the watertight compartments?" The senator seemed particularly interested in the marital status of Fleet, the lookout, who was saved. Fleet, puzzled, growled aside, "Wot questions they're arskin' me!"

The report of Lord Mersey, wreck commissioner in the British Board of Trade's investigation, was **tersely** damning.

The *Titanic* had carried boats enough for 1,178 persons, only one-third of her capacity. Her sixteen boats and four collapsibles had saved but 711 persons; 400 people had needlessly lost their lives. The boats had been but partly loaded; officers in charge of launching them had been afraid the falls would break or the boats buckle under their rated loads; boat crews had been slow in reaching their stations; launching arrangements were confused because no boat drill had been held; passengers were loaded into

farcical absurd; ridiculous
tersely short and curt

the boats haphazardly because no boat assignments had been made.

But that was not all. Lord Mersey found that sufficient warnings of ice on the steamer track had reached the *Titanic*, that her speed of twenty-two knots was "excessive under the circumstances," that "in view of the high speed at which the vessel was running it is not considered that the lookout was sufficient," and that her master made "a very **grievous** mistake"—but should not be blamed for negligence. Captain Rostron of the *Carpathia* was highly praised. "He did the very best that could be done." The *Californian* was damned. The testimony of her master, officers, and crew showed that she was not, at the most, more than nineteen miles away from the sinking *Titanic* and probably no more than five to ten miles distant. She had seen the *Titanic*'s lights; she had seen the rockets; she had not received the CQD calls because her radio operator was asleep. She had attempted to get in communication with the ship she had sighted by flashing a light, but vainly.

"The night was clear," reported Lord Mersey, "and the sea was smooth. When she first saw the rockets, the *Californian* could have pushed through the ice to the open without any serious risk and so have come to the assistance of the *Titanic*. Had she done so she might have saved many if not all of the lives that were lost.

"She made no attempt." ❖

....

grievous severe

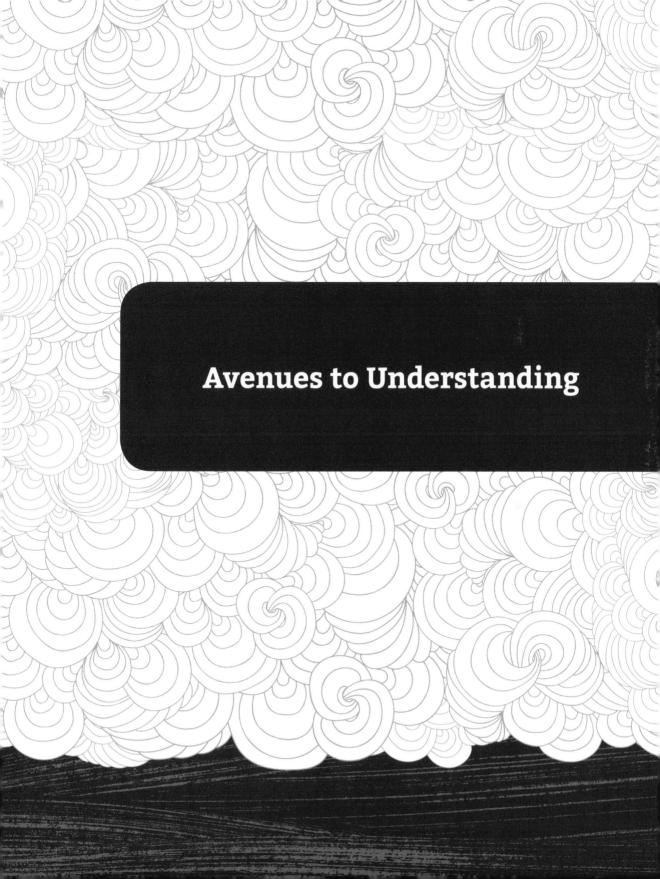

Avenues to Understanding

Daniel Hale Williams

Healing a Wounded Heart: Daniel Hale Williams

by William Orem

Chicago, 1893, a quiet summer evening—a man, his face **clenched** in agony, his shirt stained with blood, stumbles through the doors of Provident Hospital.

Fortunately for the wounded man, who was black, this hospital gave care to patients of any color—which was more than could be said of many of the hospitals in the city, indeed, in the whole United States.

Provident Hospital had been founded in 1891 by Dr. Daniel Hale Williams. Williams himself had come a long way before founding the hospital. He was born in Pennsylvania in 1856, before the Civil War, at a time when almost four million African Americans in the United States were still slaves. Daniel's parents, however, were not

....

clenched held tightly

slaves. His father owned a barbershop. As a boy, Daniel started to learn the shoemaking trade. Later, he worked in barbershops as well. All the while, he studied hard and read constantly in order to learn all that he could.

As a young man, Daniel Hale Williams worked as an apprentice to a well-respected surgeon, Dr. Henry Palmer. This apprenticeship prepared Williams to enter Chicago Medical School, one of the best medical schools in the nation at the time. After three years of hard work, Williams graduated with his **M.D.** degree in 1883.

When Dr. Williams set up his medical practice, there were only three other black doctors in Chicago. He worked at the South Side **Dispensary**, where he was often called upon to make use of his skills in surgery. He also provided medical care for children at a nearby orphanage and taught **anatomy** at the medical college where he had studied.

Wherever he looked, Dr. Williams saw few opportunities for African Americans to enter medical professions. He also saw that black people were sometimes refused medical care, or did not receive the same quality of care available to white people. That is why, when the Reverend Louis Reynolds came to him with an idea, Dr. Williams saw the wisdom of it. They would start their own hospital—a place

M.D. *Medicinae Doctor* (Latin) = Doctor of Medicine
dispensary a place where medicine or medical treatment is given out
anatomy the scientific study of the parts and structures of living things

where black people could get the same quality treatment as white people. The hospital would also serve as a training school for nurses—a goal dear to the heart of Reverend Reynolds, whose sister wanted to become a nurse but had been rejected from existing schools simply because she was black.

With support from other clergymen, wealthy donors, and community residents, Provident Hospital opened its doors in May of 1891. It gave patients equal access to quality care, and doctors and nurses equal access to quality training. In fact, Provident was the first hospital in the United States in which black and white doctors worked together to care for all patients, regardless of race.

On the summer night that the man with the knife wound stumbled into Provident Hospital, Dr. Williams was called in. The doctor reassured the patient with his calm, dignified manner. Williams was confident that he could help. But then he saw the wound—it went deep into the chest, perhaps into the heart.

At this time, the X-ray machine had not been invented, so there was no way for Dr. Williams to look inside the patient to determine the extent of the injury. No way, that is, except to open the man's chest and look right into it.

Open the chest? In 1893, doctors operated on torn muscles, on broken bones, even on serious knife wounds to other parts of the body. But they did not perform heart surgery. Many doctors argued that it was too dangerous;

Provident Hospital, founded in 1891

they said a surgeon would be foolish even to try such a thing.

Yes, it was dangerous. But Daniel Hale Williams was not foolish—on the contrary, he was very careful. He knew that, unless he took this risk, the patient was almost sure to die.

With several other doctors observing and assisting, Dr. Williams started the operation. He cut into the man's chest. He cut even deeper. He examined the depth of the stab wound. He found and repaired a torn blood vessel. He stitched up the pericardium, a fluid-filled bag that surrounds the heart. He very carefully cleaned the wound and the chest cavity, to make sure that no infection set in. Then he stitched closed the man's chest, again taking great care to keep everything as **antiseptic** as he could.

....

antiseptic free of germs

The surgery was a success. The wounded man lived, not only for the rest of that day, or the rest of that week, but for decades afterward. Dr. Williams had given him back his life. In the process, he became the first doctor to perform successful heart surgery.

Dr. Williams wasn't trying to become a hero on that evening in 1893, nor could he have known he was going to become famous for his accomplishment. But the newspapers let the world know, in dramatic headlines that read, "Sewed Up His Heart!"

Dr. Williams went on to become chief surgeon at the Freedman's Hospital in Washington, D.C. He reorganized the hospital and made it into a model of high quality medical care.

Daniel Hale Williams was successful in many ways. He worked hard to become a doctor at a time when the doors of the medical profession were generally closed to African Americans. He remained committed to his belief that all people deserve quality health care. And as a surgeon, he was bold enough to take risks but careful enough to **ensure** the safety of his patients. ❖

---

ensure to guarantee or make sure

Marie Curie

Marie Curie and the Discovery of Radioactivity

by Mara Rockliff

"Marie! It's here!" shouted Pierre. "Our shipment has arrived!"

Marie Curie did not even pause to grab her hat. She rushed out into the street after her husband. There it was—a big, heavy wagon, like the ones that brought much-needed coal for their lab's **dilapidated** stove. But this wagon carried a far more precious and exciting load.

A moment later, people passing by the School of **Physics** and Chemistry were treated to a sight not often seen on the fashionable streets of Paris in the early 1900s: a bareheaded young woman in a laboratory smock, ripping eagerly into the pile of heavy sacks and burying her hands in...*dirt?*

dilapidated run-down; neglected and in poor condition
physics a branch of science concerned with the relationship between matter and energy

To the Austrian mine owners who had sent the **pitchblende ore**, it was just dirt. After all, they had already taken out the valuable part—the metallic element called uranium—and dumped what was left over in a nearby pine forest. If a pair of **eccentric** French scientists wanted them to scoop up the worthless stuff and ship it, the mine owners were happy to **oblige**.

But Marie and Pierre Curie knew the secret of the dull brown ore. Hidden deep within it was a new chemical element. No one, the Curies included, had ever seen this element. Still, the husband-and-wife team had given it a name: radium. And Marie was determined to prove radium was real.

No one knew how difficult the task would be. But Marie, although still a student, had already shown that she possessed the most important quality of a successful scientist. When it came to the search for knowledge, she never gave up.

When she was growing up in Russian-occupied Poland, even to study science was forbidden. Many nights, young Maria Sklodowska (as she was then named) slipped through the dark streets of Warsaw on her way to an illegal night school, glancing anxiously over her shoulder for any sign

....

pitchblende a brownish-black mineral that is uncommonly high in radioactive elements
ore rock or mineral from which a valuable element may be extracted
eccentric odd; unusual in one's behavior
oblige to help

Marie Curie, in her laboratory
with husband Pierre Curie, 1903

of the Russian police. Days, she worked teaching children,
saving her rubles to send her older sister to medical school
in the city of intellectual freedom—Paris, France.

At last, her own turn came. Her sister, newly married,
sent for Marie to join her in Paris. Clutching a blanket
and a folding chair—the fourth-class train ticket, all she
could afford, did not provide even a seat—she hugged the
rest of her family goodbye. When Marie arrived in Paris
in 1891, she studied physics at the greatest university in
Europe, the Sorbonne. But how poor she was! And how
poorly prepared! She barely knew enough French, let alone
advanced math and science, to understand the lectures.

Marie studied late into the evenings in the library, struggling to catch up with her classmates. Then she climbed the six flights to her little room. In the winter, it was so cold that she emptied her closet, piling the clothes on her bed so she'd be warm enough to sleep. Sometimes she had no money to buy even an egg or a loaf of bread. But then, how could she take the time to stop studying long enough to cook?

Her hard work was rewarded. Marie won her degree in physics, graduating first in her class. And the next year she earned a second degree, in mathematics. She also met the man who soon became her husband—Pierre Curie, a brilliant young physicist as promising (and as poor) as Marie. Their love for each other was equaled only by their shared love of science.

It was a thrilling time to be a scientist. The year the Curies were married, 1895, a German physicist named Wilhelm Roentgen discovered a new kind of ray that could be used to "see" inside people and photograph their bones. He called them X-rays. The X stood for "unknown."

Not long after, the French physicist Henri Becquerel discovered that uranium let out another type of ray. These rays were weak compared to X-rays, and even Becquerel himself did not think his discovery of much importance. But Marie found the rays fascinating. Where did they come from? How were they produced? She decided to examine these mysterious "Becquerel rays" for her advanced research.

She set to work. Day after day, Marie experimented with uranium under all kinds of conditions: dry and wet; powdered and solid; pure and mixed with other elements. She heated the uranium, and shone lights on it. Then, using a special instrument called an electrometer, which Pierre and his brother had invented, she measured the uranium rays and carefully copied the numbers down in her notebook.

The results were astonishing. It didn't seem to matter what she did to the uranium. Nothing affected the strength of the rays—nothing but the amount of uranium present. The energy appeared to come from inside the metal itself, deep down at the level of its atoms. Marie named this atomic energy *radioactivity*. A substance that emitted this energy was called *radioactive*.

Her experiments yielded a second surprise. A sample of uranium-rich pitchblende turned out to be three or four times as radioactive as pure uranium. How could this be? Marie had already tested every known element in pitchblende. None was radioactive. But something in that pitchblende, something besides the uranium, was sending out rays.

There could only be one answer. If the extra radioactivity could not be coming from any known element, it must be coming from an *unknown* element.

Pierre was so excited by Marie's discovery that he dropped his own research on crystals to assist her. They knew the new element, which they decided to call radium, must be extremely tiny to have escaped notice all these years. Maybe it made up as little of the pitchblende as one percent! And yet this tiny bit of radium gave off stronger rays than a much larger amount of uranium. It must be powerfully radioactive.

The mine owners had sent them seven tons of pitchblende. Somewhere in that seven tons, Pierre and Marie were convinced, they would find radium.

It was like searching for a needle in a very large haystack—except that they had no way of knowing what this "needle" even looked like. And the needle would turn out to be much smaller than either of them imagined. It was not one percent. It was less than one *millionth* of one percent.

No one paid the Curies to do this work. They could not even persuade the School of Physics, where Pierre taught, to let them use a laboratory. Instead, they were forced to set up shop in an abandoned shed.

A visitor once described the Curies' laboratory as "a cross between a stable and a potato cellar." In summer, the heat was **stifling**. In winter, the old stove barely gave out enough warmth to thaw their frozen hands. The roof leaked when it rained.

....

stifling extremely stuffy, hot, and uncomfortable

"Yet," Marie would write years later, "it was in this miserable old shed that we passed the best and happiest years of our life, devoting our entire days to our work."

The work could be backbreaking. Marie spent many hours boiling down pitchblende in enormous pots, stirring the heavy mixture with an iron rod as tall as she was, gasping and coughing from the fumes. Later, she faced the nearly impossible task of producing purer and purer samples in the drafty, dusty shed with its dirt floor.

A year, two years, three years. Marie edged closer to her goal. Sometimes, in the evenings, she and Pierre put their little daughter to bed, leaving her in the care of her grandfather. Then the couple would walk arm in arm through the Paris streets, returning to their darkened laboratory to gaze at the old wooden tables full of tubes and bottles glowing with a faint blue light.

Finally, one day in 1902, they were able to make their announcement to the world. Marie and Pierre Curie had a pure sample of a new element called radium, thousands of times more radioactive than uranium. And it was useful. While Marie had labored to purify radium, Pierre had been experimenting with her samples. He discovered that radium could kill cancer cells. Compared to surgery or to chemicals used to treat cancer at the time, radium was much safer and more effective.

Radium rapidly became big business. A single gram was worth $100,000. Manufacturers made their fortunes making and selling radium, using the methods Marie had developed. But Marie and Pierre refused to charge a penny for their discovery. They believed that the true spirit of science meant sharing knowledge freely.

The discovery of radioactivity would turn out to be useful in many ways. For example, among other things, doctors now use radioactive dyes to help diagnose medical problems, and scientists can use radioactivity to determine the age of fossils.

In 1903 Marie became Doctor Marie Curie. The professors who judged her work—outstanding scientists themselves—told her that no advanced research had ever made such a great contribution to science.

Later that same year, she earned an even higher honor for her research. Along with Henri Becquerel, the Curies were awarded the Nobel Prize for physics. Marie Curie became the first woman ever to win a Nobel Prize.

She would go on to win a second Nobel Prize, in chemistry, making her the first person ever to be awarded the Nobel Prize twice. And the Sorbonne made her its first female professor. But all these "firsts" meant little to Marie Curie. For her, what came first was always science. ❖

Marie Curie with President Warren G. Harding at the White House, May 20, 1921

1921: Marie Curie
Visits the U.S.

from National Institute of Standards and Technology

By the end of World War I, Marie Curie was probably the most famous woman in the world. She had made a conscious decision, however, not to patent radium or its medical applications. As the price of radium **escalated**, she found that she did not have sufficient supplies for the radiochemical investigations that she wanted to undertake at the Institute of Radium in Paris.

. . . .

escalated rose

As for the radium prepared by me out of the ore we managed to obtain in the first years of our work, I have given it all to my laboratory.

*The price of radium is very high since it is found in minerals in very small quantities, and the profits of its manufacture have been great, as this substance is used to cure a number of diseases. So it is a fortune which we have sacrificed in **renouncing** the exploitation of our discovery, a fortune that could, after us, have gone to our children. But what is even more to be considered is the objection of our many friends, who have argued, not without reason, that if we had guaranteed our rights, we could have had the financial means of founding a satisfactory Institute of Radium, without experiencing any of the difficulties that have been such a handicap to both of us, and are still a handicap to me. Yet, I still believe that we have done right.*

Marie Curie

Her benefactress was an American woman, Mrs. W. B. Meloney. Mrs. Meloney launched a campaign to have the women of America contribute $100,000 to buy a gram of radium for presentation to Marie Curie for her use at the Institute of Radium.

....

renouncing giving up

Thus, in 1921 Marie Curie made her first visit to the United States accompanied by her two daughters, Irène and Eve. Irène Curie's contributions to radium science will be mentioned later. The younger daughter, Eve, became an author, and her 1938 book, *Madame Curie: A Biography by Eve Curie*, gives a thorough account of their trip to the United States. One stop was the Radium Refining Plant in Pittsburgh, where Marie Curie toured the chemical extraction facilities used to prepare radium for the U.S. market....

On May 20, 1921, Marie Curie visited the White House to receive the gift of the gram of radium from President Harding. The hazardous source itself was not brought to the ceremony. Instead, she was presented with a golden key to the **coffer** and a certificate. A replica of the coffer with dummy radium tubes was set on a table in the East Room of the White House during the ceremony. As the document indicates, it was a Certificate for Radioactive Material submitted for measurement and certification to the National Bureau of Standards. It was signed by Samuel W. Stratton, the Director of the Bureau, which was then as now a part of the Department of Commerce. This was not a standard source, but was intended for research purposes. Accordingly, it was subdivided into ten, **hermetically**

---

coffer a box or chest designed to hold valuable objects
hermetically in an airtight way

sealed, glass tubes of about 100 mg each. The certification was presumably made by gamma-ray comparisons with the NBS radium standard (Secondary Standard No. 6). "The residual uncertainty in the numerical value of the radium element equivalent of these several specimens does not exceed 0.7 of one percent."

The radium was packaged for shipment at NBS and loaded on to the ship for the return trip to France. The box used for the shipment resides in the Curie Museum in Paris. Although Marie Curie's visit to the White House is recorded in great detail, very little is known about her contacts with the NBS. There is, however, her own report in the biography of Pierre Curie (p. 117). "I have visited with special interest the Bureau of Standards, a very important national institution in Washington for scientific measurements and for study connected with them. The tubes of radium presented to me were at the Bureau, whose officials had kindly offered to make measurements, and to take care of the packing and delivery to the ship." ❖

The Inchcape Rock

by Robert Southey

No **stir** in the air, no stir in the sea,
The ship was as still as she could be;
Her sails from heaven received no motion;
Her **keel** was steady in the ocean.

Without either sign or sound of their shock
The waves flowed over the Inchcape Rock;
So little they rose, so little they fell,
They did not move the Inchcape Bell.

The good old **Abbot** of Aberbrothok
Had placed that bell on the Inchcape Rock;
On a **buoy** in the storm it floated and swung,
And over the waves its warning rung.

When the rock was hid by the **surges'** swell,
The **mariners** heard the warning bell;
And then they knew the **perilous** rock
And blessed the Abbot of Aberbrothok.

....

stir movement
keel the center beam running under a ship
abbot a leader of a monastery
buoy a floating object in water used to mark a route or indicate danger
surges waves
mariners sailors
perilous dangerous

The sun in heaven was shining gay,—
All things were joyful on that day;
The sea birds screamed as they wheeled around,
And there was **joyance** in their sound.

The buoy of the Inchcape Bell was seen,
A darker spot on the ocean green;
Sir Ralph the Rover walked his deck
And he fixed his eye on the darker speck.

He felt the cheering power of spring,—
It made him whistle, it made him sing;
His heart was **mirthful** to excess,
But the Rover's mirth was wickedness.

His eye was on the Inchcape float.
Quoth he, "My men, put out the boat
And row me to the Inchcape Rock,
And I'll **plague** the Abbot of Aberbrothok."

The boat is lowered, the boatmen row,
And to the Inchcape Rock they go;
Sir Ralph bent over from the boat,
And he cut the bell from the Inchcape float.

---

joyance delight; joy
mirthful happy; gleeful
plague to annoy or bother

Down sank the bell with a gurgling sound;
The bubbles rose and burst around.
Quoth Sir Ralph, "The next who comes to the Rock
Won't bless the Abbot of Aberbrothok."

Sir Ralph the Rover sail'd away,—
He **scoured** the seas for many a day;
And now, grown rich with **plundered** store,
He steers his course for Scotland's shore.

So thick a haze o'erspreads the sky
They cannot see the sun on high;
The wind hath blown a gale all day;
At evening it hath died away.

On the deck the Rover takes his stand;
So dark it is they see no land.
Quoth Sir Ralph, "It will be lighter soon,
For there is the dawn of the rising moon."

"Canst hear," said one, "the breakers roar?
Methinks we should be near the shore."
"Now where we are I cannot tell,
But I wish I could hear the Inchcape Bell."

scoured searched
plundered stolen; taken by force

They hear no sound; the swell is strong;
Though the wind hath fallen, they drift along
Till the vessel strikes with a shivering shock,
Full on the ledge of the Inchcape Rock!

Sir Ralph the Rover tore his hair;
He **curst** himself in his despair;
The waves rush in on every side—
The ship is sinking beneath the tide.

But even in his dying fear
One dreadful sound could the Rover hear,—
A sound as if, with the Inchcape Bell,
The Devil below was ringing his knell. ❖

curst cursed

The Bell Rock

by P. J. A. Burt, Natural Resources Institute,
University of Greenwich

"Without either sign or sound of their shock,
The waves flowed over the Inchcape Rock"
(Southey).

The Bell Rock is well known as a former coastal station
for the inshore shipping forecast. This name, however,
masks a fascinating history of piracy, civil engineering,
poetry, literature and **meteorological** observation.

The Rock lies approximately 12 miles (19 km) south-
east of Arbroath on the eastern coast of Scotland (56° 26′N,
02° 23′W) and marks the upper part of a sandstone reef
which is submerged at high tide. Formerly known as the
Inchcape, or Inchscape, Rock (Johnston 1970) the position
of the Rock makes it a prime trap for shipping. Any vessels

---

meteorological relating to the study of the atmosphere and weather

sailing into or out of the Firth of Tay, and thus to or from the major port of Dundee, are liable to encounter it, or risk being wrecked on the coast in an attempt to avoid it. Although it is uncovered at low tide, the Rock is completely hidden by around 5 m or more of water at high tide or when it is stormy. It has been calculated that by the early 1800s the winter toll on shipping was around six ships per winter (Bathurst 2000).

The danger of the Inchcape Rock was recognised for centuries. In the late 1300s, the Abbott of Arbroath (at that time the town was called Aberbrothock) attached a bell to the Rock in such a way that the bell floated on the tide as it rose and fell, thereby sounding a warning to approaching shipping (Keay and Keay 1994; Bathurst 2000). This gave rise to the alternative name of the Inchcape Rock—Bell Rock. Legend tells of a pirate who, for amusement, cut the bell from its mooring, only to be wrecked on the Rock himself some time later. This story has been immortalised in Robert Southey's poem "The Inchcape Rock" (Phoenix Poetry 2002). The date when the poem was written is unclear; dates between 1796 and 1815 have been cited in the literature, but the poem was finally published in 1820 (Taylor 2003). Southey named the pirate as Ralph the Rover, but contemporary Scottish accounts suggest that the pirate was a Dutchman who was intent on using the Rock as a means to trap shipping, which could then be plundered (Bathurst 2000). Whilst the true historical background to these events may never be fully untangled, it is clear that by the early 1800s the Rock was recognised as a major hazard, a fact reinforced as a consequence of a three-day storm in 1799 in which some 70 ships were wrecked around the Scottish coast, including a number on the Rock (Bathurst 2000), and the loss of HMS *York* on Inchcape in 1804. Attempts were made to place wooden **beacons** on the Rock, but these did not survive for more than a few months (Keay and Keay 1994; Bathurst 2000).

At the time of the 1799 storm, the chief engineer of the Northern Lighthouse Board (NLB) (the body tasked with the erection and maintenance of lighthouses around the coast of Scotland) was Robert Stevenson. Stevenson's stepfather, Thomas Smith, had also been chief engineer of the NLB and had worked to develop improved lighting systems for lighthouses (Bathurst 2000). After much lobbying, Stevenson's plan for a permanent lighthouse on the Rock was accepted by the NLB and construction commenced in 1807. The story of the building of the lighthouse is told by Bathurst (2000), to which the reader is referred for a more detailed account. The lighthouse took almost four years to complete, primarily as work was restricted to the summer months; winter weather precluded any building on, and often travel to, the Rock. Built in 90 masonry courses, the bottom third of the structure was constructed from an outer lining of Aberdeen and

---

beacons lights or other visible objects used as warnings or signals

Peterhead granite, with inner layers of sandstone, the rest of the structure from sandstone alone (Taylor 2003). The unworked rock was shipped by sea to Arbroath, where it was unloaded, taken by horse and cart to a masonry yard where it was shaped and dovetailed, and then pulled back to Arbroath harbour, again by horse and cart, for transport by small boat to the Rock and assembly (Keay and Keay 1994). Despite the rigors of the task, only two lives were lost during construction. The 120 ft (36 m) tall completed lighthouse was first illuminated in February 1811, making it the oldest rock lighthouse in the British Isles (Keay and Keay 1994; Bathurst 2000; NLB 2003) (see Fig. 1). Initially operating on a four-minute cycle, the alternating red and white flash had a range of 35 miles (56 km) and could be seen from the main north–south east coast road, from just north of Arbroath to Fife Ness.

The lighthouse received a major overhaul in 1902, when the lighting system was replaced and the timing of the light was changed to a red and white flash every 60 seconds. Further renovation in 1964 updated the lighting system by providing diesel and electric generators to power the light, as well as **refurbishing** the crew's living quarters (Taylor 2003).

The lighthouse keepers started to make weather observations for the Met Office after an anemograph was

....

refurbishing renovating and repairing or improving

installed in 1928 (the exact time after this that observations commenced is uncertain). Observations continued until 1987, with an interruption from early 1939 to late 1945 as a consequence of the Second World War (when the lighthouse survived three separate attacks by aircraft (Taylor 2003). The Met Office Archives in Edinburgh hold a detailed record of observational activities and equipment repairs during the lighthouse's time as a weather reporting station. The following highlights are extracted from those records.

Fig. 1 The Bell Rock Lighthouse

Measurements of air pressure, wind speed, wind direction, and air temperature were routinely made. The keepers also reported visibility, based on sightings of surface features on the Rock (tide-dependent) and the sight of the Scottish coastline, cloud height and cloud cover. Over time, attempts were made to record sea temperatures, but these were recognised as being unreliable, primarily due to problems of access (sea water had to be collected in a bucket and pulled up to the lighthouse), but also as a consequence of temperature variations due to solar heating of the Rock at low tide warming the sea water as it covered the Rock at high tide. Air temperature data were collected from a screen 84 feet (c. 25 m) above mean high water (spring); a distant-reading thermograph was installed in 1946. Observations of temperature ceased in 1972. A new anemograph was installed in 1955 after it was noted that the bullet holes in the wind vane, caused by the aerial attacks over 10 years earlier, had not been repaired! The vane of the new unit was 124 feet (c. 40 m) above mean sea-level. Weather data were transmitted to RAF Leuchars in Fife (the nearest RAF station). These improvements continued with the supply of new equipment, and maintenance, as required. The daily observing times also changed throughout around 50 years of data collection, often in response to specific demands (for example, accommodating changes in the time of BBC weather broadcasts in 1960 and the requirements of the shipping bulletin). Regular observations at the synoptic times commenced in December 1945, with additional reports for 0900, 1500 and 2100 GMT being made by 1954. An additional daily observation at 2200 GMT had started by 1982, with hourly observations from late December 1985.

The interior of the lighthouse was badly damaged by fire in September 1987, although the superstructure was not affected. Shortly before this the operation of the light had begun to be **automated**, and by mid-1988 the lighthouse

---

automated operated by machines

was unmanned. As part of the automation process, the signal from the lighthouse was replaced with a white light, flashing once every five seconds, with a theoretical visibility of 18 miles (29 km) (NLB 2003) and the Rock ceased to be a coastal weather observing and recording station. Observations from the lighthouse at St. Abbs Head replaced those from Bell Rock in the shipping forecast win April 1989.

Perhaps more than any other lighthouse (with the possible exception of the Flannan Isles, west of the Isle of Lewis, built by Robert Stevenson's grandsons David and Charles), the Bell Rock has inspired poetry and prose. In addition to Southey's poem, set long before the lighthouse was built, the lighthouse also inspired a second, less well-known, verse shortly after completion, when Sir Walter Scott visited the lighthouse in 1814, and wrote the poem, "Pharos loquitur" ("the lighthouse speaks") in the visitor's book. The author R. M. Ballantyne (who wrote *The coral island*) stayed in the lighthouse for three weeks to gather background material for his story *The lighthouse* (Ballantyne 1865), which he set on the Bell Rock. Although the story is out of print in paper format, it is now available on the WWW, republished by Athelstane. Robert Stevenson commissioned the artist J. M. W. Turner to paint a picture of the lighthouse, which Stevenson used to illustrate his book *Account of the Bell Rock lighthouse*, published in 1824 (Bathurst 2000). Remarkably, Turner painted the picture, now housed in the National Gallery of Scotland, without visiting the lighthouse! More recently, the lighthouse featured in a set of commemorative stamps issued by the Post Office in March 1998.

What of the other major players in this story? Robert Stevenson went on to design many other lighthouses around the Scottish coast, and all three of his sons who survived infancy became lighthouse engineers, as did several of his grandsons. As a family they were responsible for the construction of almost 90 lighthouses (Erraid 2003). Robert Stevenson's son, Thomas, also developed the Stevenson screen (Meteorological Office 1972), whilst Thomas's son, although initially destined for a career in engineering, became an author, Robert Louis Stevenson. One remaining 'relic' of the lighthouse is the skeleton of the horse, Bassey, who pulled the quarried and cut stones to the harbour at Arbroath, which is now believed to be in the University of St. Andrews' Bell-Pettigrew Museum (Burt 1977).

Acknowledgements

I am most grateful...to Elizabeth Kerr, Met Office, Saughton House, Edinburgh, for providing me with the station history of the Bell Rock observing station; and also to Professor Roger Knight, Greenwich Maritime Institute, University of Greenwich, for clarification of issues surrounding the early nineteenth-century shipwrecks.

References

Ballantyne, R. M. (1865) *The lighthouse.*
Published in electronic format by Athelstane E-Texts,
http://www.athelstane.co.uk/ballanty/light_ho/light_ho.txt

Bathurst, B. (2000) *The lighthouse Stevensons.*
Omnia Books Ltd, Glasgow

Burt, D. R. R. (1977) *Guide to the Bell-Pettigrew Museum.*
University of St. Andrews, Scotland

Erraid (2003) Erraid Island website.
http://www.erraid.fslife.co.uk/pages/Bell%20Rock%20
Lighthouse%20-%20The%20Stevensons.htm

Johnston, J. B. (1970) *Place-names of Scotland.*
Lewis Reprints Ltd, Port Talbot

Keay, J. and Keay, J. (1994) *Collins encyclopedia of Scotland.*
HarperCollins, London

Meteorological Office (1972) *Meteorological glossary.*
Her Majesty's Stationery Office, London

NLB (2003) http://www.nlb.org.uk/ourlights/history/bellrock.htm

Phoenix Poetry (2002) *Poetry please.* Clays Ltd, St. Ives

Taylor, D. (2003) Bell Rock Lighthouse: a reference site.
http://www.bellrock.org.uk

Correspondence to: Dr P. J. A. Burt, Natural Resources Institute,
University of Greenwich at Medway, Central Avenue, Chatham,
Kent ME4 4TB. e-mail: P.J.A.Burt@greenwich.ac.uk ©
Royal Meteorological Society, 2004. doi: 10.1256/wea.224. ❖

Latin & Soul

by Victor Hernández Cruz

1

some waves

     a wave of now

          a trombone speaking to you

a piano is trying to break a **molecule**

is trying to lift the stage into orbit

around the red spotlights

a shadow

the shadows   of dancers

dancers   they are dancing   falling

out that space   made for dancing

they should dance

on the tables   they should

dance inside of their drinks

they should dance on the

ceiling they should dance/dance

thru universes

leaning-moving

     we are traveling

----

molecule a submicroscopic group of atoms that, joined together, represents the smallest possible unit of a chemical compound

where are we going

if we only knew

with this rhythm   with
this banging   with   fire
with this   all   this   O
my god i wonder   where are
we going
       sink into a room full of laughter
       full of happiness   full of life
       those dancers
       the dancers
       are clapping their hands
       stomping their feet

hold back them tears
              all those sentimental stories
cooked uptown   if you can   hold it for after

we are going
       away-away-away
       beyond these wooden tables
       beyond these red lights
       beyond these rugs & paper
       walls beyond way past
       i mean way past them clouds
       over the buildings   over the
       rivers   over towns   over cities

like on rails   but faster   like
a train   but smoother
away past stars
bursting with drums.

2

a sudden misunderstanding

                    a cloud

                    full of grayness

a body thru a store window

                    a hand reaching

                    into the back

                              pocket

a scream

        a piano is talking to you
        thru all this
        why don't you answer it. ❖

The Cremation of Sam McGee

by Robert Service

There are strange things done in the midnight sun
*   By the men who **moil** for gold;*
The Arctic trails have their secret tales
*   That would make your blood run cold;*
The Northern Lights have seen queer sights,
*   But the queerest they ever did see*
*Was that night on the **marge** of Lake Lebarge*
*   I **cremated** Sam McGee.*

Now Sam McGee was from Tennessee,
    where the cotton blooms and blows.
Why he left his home in the South to roam
    'round the Pole, God only knows.
He was always cold, but the land of gold
    seemed to hold him like a spell;
Though he'd often say in his **homely** way
    that he'd "sooner live in hell."

....

moil to toil or work hard
marge margin; edge
cremated burned a dead body
homely plain; simple

On a Christmas Day we were **mushing** our way
    over the Dawson trail.
Talk of your cold! through the **parka**'s fold
    it stabbed like a driven nail.
If our eyes we'd close, then the lashes froze
    till sometimes we couldn't see,
It wasn't much fun, but the only one
    to whimper was Sam McGee.

And that very night, as we lay packed tight
    in our robes beneath the snow,
And the dogs were fed, and the stars o'erhead
    were dancing heel and toe,
He turned to me, and "Cap," says he,
    "I'll cash in this trip, I guess;
And if I do, I'm asking that you
    won't refuse my last request."

Well, he seemed so low that I couldn't say no;
    then he says with a sort of moan,
"It's the cursed cold, and it's got right hold
    till I'm chilled clean through to the bone.
Yet 'tain't being dead—it's my awful dread
    of the icy grave that pains;
So I want you to swear that, foul or fair,
    you'll cremate my last remains."

mushing driving dogs over snow
parka a warm coat with a hood

A pal's last need is a thing to heed,
    so I swore I would not fail;
And we started on at the streak of dawn;
    but God! he looked **ghastly** pale.
He crouched on the sleigh, and he raved all day
    of his home in Tennessee;
And before nightfall a **corpse** was all
    that was left of Sam McGee.

There wasn't a breath in that land of death,
    and I hurried, horror-driven,
With a corpse half hid that I couldn't get rid,
    because of a promise given;
It was **lashed** to the sleigh, and it seemed to say:
    "You may **tax** your brawn and brains,
But you promised true, and it's up to you
    to cremate these last remains."

Now a promise made is a debt unpaid,
    and the trail has its own stern code.
In the days to come, though my lips were **dumb**,
    in my heart how I cursed that load!
In the long, long night, by the lone firelight,
    while the huskies, round in a ring,

....

ghastly horribly; terrifyingly
corpse a dead body
lashed tied tightly
tax to make hard demands on
dumb unable to speak; silent

Howled out their woes to the homeless snows—
 O God, how I **loathed** the thing!

And every day that quiet clay
 seemed to heavy and heavier grow;
And on I went, though the dogs were **spent**
 and the **grub** was getting low.
The trail was bad, and I felt half mad,
 but I swore I would not give in;
And I'd often sing to the hateful thing,
 and it **hearkened** with a grin.

Till I came to the marge of Lake Lebarge,
 and a **derelict** there lay;
It was jammed in the ice, but I saw **in a trice**
 it was called the *Alice May*.
And I looked at it, and I thought a bit,
 and I looked at my frozen chum;
Then "Here," said I, with a sudden cry,
 "is my cre-ma-tor-eum."

Some planks I tore from the cabin floor,
 and I lit the boiler fire;

loathed hated
spent exhausted; worn out
grub food
hearkened listened
derelict something abandoned (in this case, a deserted ship)
in a trice an expression meaning "in an instant"

Some coal I found that was lying around,
    and I heaped the fuel higher;
The flames just soared, and the furnace roared—
    such a blaze you seldom see,
And I burrowed a hole in the glowing coal,
    and I stuffed in Sam McGee.

Then I made a hike, for I didn't like
    to hear him sizzle so;
And the heavens scowled, and the huskies howled,
    and the wind began to blow.
It was icy cold, but the hot sweat rolled
    down my cheeks, and I don't know why;
And the greasy smoke in an inky cloak
    went streaking down the sky.

I do not know how long in the snow
    I wrestled with **grisly** fear;
But the stars came out and they danced about
    ere again I **ventured** near;
I was sick with dread, but I bravely said,
    "I'll just take a peep inside.
I guess he's cooked, and it's time I looked."
    Then the door I opened wide.

....

grisly terrifying
ere an old-fashioned word for "before"
ventured proceeded in something risky

And there sat Sam, looking cool and calm,
    in the heart of the furnace roar;
And he wore a smile you could see a mile,
    and he said, "Please close that door.
It's fine in here, but I greatly fear
    you'll let in the cold and storm—
Since I left Plumtree, down in Tennessee,
    it's the first time I've been warm."

There are strange things done in the midnight sun
    By the men who moil for gold;
The Arctic trails have their secret tales
    That would make your blood run cold;
The Northern Lights have seen queer sights,
    But the queerest they ever did see
Was that night on the marge of Lake Lebarge
    I cremated Sam McGee. ❖

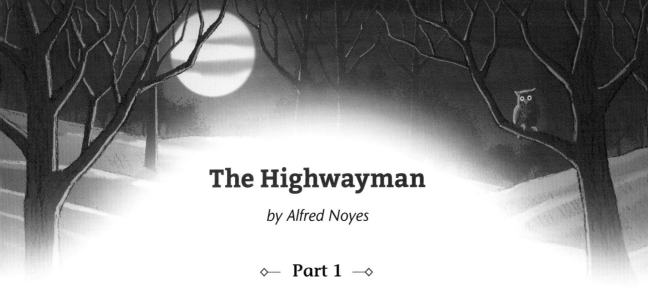

The Highwayman

by Alfred Noyes

◇— Part 1 —◇

The wind was a **torren** of darkness among the gusty trees,
The moon was a ghostly **galleon** tossed upon cloudy seas,
The road was a ribbon of moonlight over the purple **moor**,
And the highwayman came riding—
    Riding—riding—
The highwayman came riding, up to the old inn-door.

He'd a French cocked-hat on his forehead, a bunch of lace
    at his chin,
A coat of the **claret** velvet, and **breeches** of brown doe-skin;
They fitted with never a wrinkle; his boots were up to
    the thigh!
And he rode with a jeweled twinkle,
    His pistol butts a-twinkle,
His **rapier hilt** a-twinkle, under the jeweled sky.

....

torrent a violent flood
galleon a large sailing ship
moor an open field or plain
claret dark purplish red (like the color of the wine called claret)

breeches knee-length pants
rapier a long sword
hilt a handle, especially of a sword

Over the **cobbles** he clattered and clashed in the dark
        inn-yard,
And he tapped with his whip on the shutters, but all was
        locked and barred:
He whistled a tune to the window, and who should be
        waiting there
But the landlord's black-eyed daughter,
    Bess, the landlord's daughter,
Plaiting a dark red love-knot into her long black hair.

And dark in the dark old inn-yard a **stable-wicket** creaked
Where Tim the **ostler** listened; his face was white
        and **peaked**;
His eyes were hollows of madness, his hair like moldy hay,
But he loved the landlord's daughter,
    The landlord's red-lipped daughter,
Dumb as a dog he listened, and he heard the robber say—

"One kiss, my bonny sweetheart, I'm after a prize to-night,
But I shall be back with the yellow gold before the morning
        light;
Yet, if they press me sharply, and **harry** me through
        the day,

---

cobbles cobblestones; round stones used in old roads
plaiting braiding
stable-wicket a gate to the stable
ostler someone who takes care of horses
peaked pale
harry to force to move along; to disturb constantly

Then look for me by moonlight,
  Watch for me by moonlight,
I'll come to thee by moonlight, though hell should bar
    the way."

He rose upright in the stirrups; he scarce could reach
    her hand,
But she loosened her hair i' the **casement**! His face burned
    like a **brand**
As the black **cascade** of perfume came tumbling over his
    breast; And he kissed its waves in the moonlight,
  (Oh, sweet black waves in the moonlight!)
Then he tugged at his rein in the moonlight, and galloped
    away to the West.

⬦— Part II —⬦

He did not come in the dawning; he did not come at noon;
And out o' the **tawny** sunset, before the rise o' the moon,
When the road was a gypsy's ribbon, looping the
    purple moor,
A red-coat troop came marching—
  Marching—marching—
King George's men came marching up to the old inn-door.

casement a window frame
brand torch; a piece of burning wood
cascade a waterfall—thus, anything that falls or rushes forth
tawny having a warm, sandy color

They said no word to the landlord, they drank his
      ale instead,
But they gagged his daughter and bound her to the foot of
      her narrow bed;
Two of them knelt at her casement, with **muskets** at
      their side!
There was death at every window,
    And hell at one dark window,
For Bess could see, through her casement, the road that
      he would ride.

They had tied her up to attention, with many a
      sniggering jest;
They had bound a musket beside her, with the barrel
      beneath her breast!
"Now keep good watch!" and they kissed her. She heard
      the dead man say—
Look for me by moonlight;
    Watch for me by moonlight;
I'll come to thee by moonlight, though hell should bar the way.

She twisted her hands behind her; but all the knots
      held good!
She writhed her hands till her fingers were wet with sweat
      or blood!

---

muskets rifles
sniggering snickering; laughing in a mean, scornful way

They stretched and strained in the darkness, and the hours
     crawled by like years,
Till, now, on the stroke of midnight,
   Cold, on the stroke of midnight,
The tip of one finger touched it! The trigger at least
     was hers!

The tip of one finger touched it; she **strove** no more for
     the rest!
Up, she stood to attention, with the barrel beneath
     her breast,
She would not risk their hearing; she would not
     strive again;
For the road lay bare in the moonlight;
   Blank and bare in the moonlight;
And the blood of her veins in the moonlight throbbed to
     her love's refrain.

Tlot-tlot, tlot-tlot! Had they heard it? The horse-hoofs
     ringing clear;
Tlot-tlot, tlot-tlot, in the distance? Were they deaf that they
     did not hear?
Down the ribbon of moonlight, over the brow of the hill,
The highwayman came riding,
   Riding, riding!

---

strove tried with great effort

The red-coats looked to their **priming**! She stood up,
    straight and still!

Tlot-tlot, in the frosty silence! *Tlot-tlot,* in the echoing night!
Nearer he came and nearer! Her face was like a light!
Her eyes grew wide for a moment; she drew one last
        deep breath,
Then her finger moved in the moonlight,
    Her musket shattered the moonlight,
Shattered her breast in the moonlight and warned
        him—with her death.

He turned; he **spurred** to the westward; he did not know
        who stood Bowed, with her head o'er the musket,
        drenched with her own red blood!
Not till the dawn he heard it, his face grew gray to hear
How Bess, the landlord's daughter,
    The landlord's black-eyed daughter,
Had watched for her love in the moonlight, and died in the
        darkness there.

Back, he spurred like a madman, shrieking a curse to
        the sky,
With the white road smoking behind him, and his rapier
        brandished high!

---

priming preparations for firing a musket
spurred urged on and directed a horse (with spurs)
brandished waved or held

Blood-red were his spurs in the golden moon; wine-red was
his velvet coat,
When they shot him down on the highway,
Down like a dog on the highway,
And he lay in his blood in the highway, with the bunch of
lace at his throat!

And still of a winter's night, they say, when the wind is in
the trees,
When the moon is a ghostly galleon tossed upon cloudy seas,
When the road is a ribbon of moonlight over the purple moor,
A highwayman comes riding—
Riding—riding—
A highwayman comes riding, up to the old inn-door.

Over the cobbles he clatters and clangs in the dark inn-yard;
And he taps with his whip on the shutters, but all is locked
and barred;
He whistles a tune to the window, and who should be
waiting there
But the landlord's black-eyed daughter,
Bess, the landlord's daughter,
Plaiting a dark red love-knot into her long black hair. ❖

Instructing, Enlightening, and Persuading

The Fish I Didn't Catch

by John Greenleaf Whittier

Our bachelor uncle who lived with us was a quiet, **genial** man, much given to hunting and fishing; and it was one of the pleasures of our young life to accompany him on his expeditions to Great Hill, Brandy-brow Woods, the Pond, and, best of all, to the Country Brook. We were quite willing to work hard in the cornfield or the haying lot to finish the necessary day's labor in season for an afternoon stroll through the woods and along the brookside.

I remember my first fishing **excursion** as if it were but yesterday. I have been happy many times in my life, but never more intensely so than when I received that first fishing pole from my uncle's hand, and **trudged** off with him through the woods and meadows. It was a still, sweet day of early summer; the long afternoon shadows of the trees lay cool across our path; the leaves seemed greener, the flowers brighter, the birds merrier, than ever before.

My uncle, who knew by long experience where were the best **haunts** of **pickerel**, considerately placed me at the most favorable point. I threw out my line as I had so often

----

genial friendly; kind
excursion a trip
trudged walked (usually with effort)
haunts places often visited
pickerel a small, freshwater fish

seen others, and waited anxiously for a bite, moving the bait in rapid jerks on the surface of the water in imitation of the leap of a frog. Nothing came of it. "Try again," said my uncle. Suddenly the bait sank out of sight. "Now for it," thought I; "here is a fish at last."

I made a strong pull, and brought up a tangle of weeds. Again and again I cast out my line with aching arms, and drew it back empty. I looked at my uncle appealingly. "Try once more," he said; "we fishermen must have patience."

Suddenly something tugged at my line, and swept off with it into deep water. Jerking it up, I saw a fine pickerel wriggling in the sun. "Uncle!" I cried, looking back in uncontrollable excitement, "I've got a fish!"

"Not yet," said my uncle. As he spoke there was splash in the water; I caught the **arrowy** gleam of a scared fish shooting into the middle of the stream—my hook hung empty from the line. I had lost my prize.

We are **apt** to speak of the sorrows of childhood as **trifles** in comparison with those of grown-up people; but we may depend upon it the young folks don't agree with us. Our griefs, modified and restrained by reason, experience, and self-respect, keep the proprieties, and, if possible, avoid a scene; but the sorrow of childhood, unreasoning and all-absorbing, is a complete abandonment to the passion.

....

arrowy like an arrow
apt likely
trifles unimportant things

The doll's nose is broken, and the world breaks up with it; the marble rolls out of sight, and the solid globe rolls off with the marble.

So, overcome with my great and bitter disappointment, I sat down on the nearest **hassock**, and for a time refused to be comforted, even by my uncle's assurance that there were more fish in the brook. He refitted my bait, and, putting the pole again in my hands, told me to try my luck once more.

"But remember, boy," he said, with his shrewd smile, "never brag of catching a fish until he is on dry ground. I've seen older folks doing that in more ways than one, and so making fools of themselves. It's no use to boast of anything until it's done, nor then, either, for it speaks for itself."

How often since I have been reminded of the fish that I did not catch. When I hear people boasting of a work as yet undone, and trying to **anticipate** the credit which belongs only to actual achievement, I call to mind that scene by the brookside, and the wise caution of my uncle in that particular instance takes the form of a **proverb** of universal application: "NEVER BRAG OF YOUR FISH BEFORE YOU CATCH HIM." ❖

----

hassock a tussock—that is, a thick clump of grass
anticipate to expect; to look forward to something as certain though it is yet to happen
proverb a short, well-known saying containing a wise thought

If

by Rudyard Kipling

If you can keep your head when all about you
    Are losing theirs and blaming it on you;
If you can trust yourself when all men doubt you,
    But **make allowance for** their doubting too;
If you can wait and not be tired by waiting,
    Or, being lied about, don't deal in lies,
Or, being hated, don't give way to hating,
    And yet don't look too good, nor talk too wise;

If you can dream—and not make dreams your master;
    If you can think—and not make thoughts your aim;
If you can meet with triumph and disaster
    And treat those two **impostors** just the same;
If you can bear to hear the truth you've spoken
    Twisted by **knaves** to make a trap for fools,
Or watch the things you gave your life to broken,
    And stoop and build 'em up with worn-out tools;

If you can make one heap of all your winnings
    And risk it on one turn of pitch-and-toss,
And lose, and start again at your beginnings

---

make allowance for to grant the possibility of
impostors deceivers; persons who try to trick by assuming a false identity
knaves tricky, dishonest people

If you can force your heart and nerve and **sinew**
    To serve your turn long after they are gone,
And so hold on when there is nothing in you
    Except the Will which says to them: "Hold on!"

If you can talk with crowds and keep your **virtue**,
    Or walk with kings—nor lose the common touch;
If neither foes nor loving friends can hurt you;
    If all men count with you, but none too much;
If you can fill the unforgiving minute
    With sixty seconds' worth of distance run—
Yours is the Earth and everything that's in it,
    And—which is more—you'll be a Man, my son! ❖

....

sinew muscle
virtue goodness; moral strength

Letter to His Son

by Robert E. Lee

You must **study** to be **frank** with the world; frankness is
the child of honesty and courage. Say just what you mean
to do on every occasion and take it for granted you meant
to do right. If a friend asks a favor, you should grant it if it
is reasonable; if not, tell him plainly why you cannot; you
will wrong him and wrong yourself by **equivocation** of any
kind. Never do a wrong thing to make a friend or keep one;
the man who requires you to do so is **dearly** purchased at
a sacrifice. Deal kindly but firmly with all your classmates;
you will find it the **policy** which wears best ...

If you have any fault to find with anyone, tell him,
not others, of what you complain; there is no more
dangerous experiment than that of undertaking to be one
thing before a man's face and another behind his back.
We should live, act, and say nothing to the injury of
anyone. It is not only best as a matter of principle but it is
the path of peace and honor.

In regard to duty, let me, in conclusion of this **hasty**
letter, inform you that nearly a hundred years ago there

---

study to try hard
frank candid; sincere
equivocation misleading or deceptive language
dearly at a very high price
policy guiding principle; plan of action
hasty hurried; quick

was a day of remarkable gloom and darkness—still known as "the dark day"—a day when the light of the sun was slowly extinguished as if by an eclipse. The Legislature of Connecticut was in session, and as the members saw the unexpected and **unaccountable** darkness coming on, they shared in the general **awe** and terror. It was supposed by many that the last day—the day of judgment—had come. Someone in the **consternation**

Robert E. Lee and son William Henry Fitzhugh Lee, c. 1845

of the hour moved an **adjournment**. Then there arose an old Puritan legislator, Davenport of Stamford, and said that if the last day had come he desired to be found in his place doing his duty and therefore moved that candles be brought in, so that the House could proceed with its duty. There was quietness in that man's mind, the quietness of heavenly wisdom and inflexible willingness to obey present duty.

Duty, then, is the **sublimest** word in our language. Do your duty in all things, like the old Puritan. You cannot do more, you should never wish to do less. Never let me and your mother wear one gray hair for any lack of duty on your part. ❖

....

unaccountable beyond any explanation; strange
awe wonder; dread
consternation state of confused amazement
adjournment a break; the ending of an activity for a time
sublimest greatest; most noble, admirable, and awe-inspiring

Mother to Son

by Langston Hughes

Well, son, I'll tell you:
Life for me ain't been no crystal stair.
It's had tacks in it,
And splinters,
And boards torn up,
And places with no carpet on the floor—
Bare.
But all the time
I'se been a-climbin' on,
And reachin' **landin's**,
And turnin' corners,
And sometimes goin' in the dark
Where there ain't been no light.
So boy, don't you turn back.
Don't you set down on the steps
'Cause you finds it's kinder hard.
Don't you fall now—
For I'se still goin', honey,
I'se still climbin',
And life for me ain't been no crystal stair. ❖

....

landin's landings, the level floors at the top or bottom of flights of stairs

What's Important

President Cleveland, Where Are You?

by Robert Cormier

That was the autumn of the cowboy cards—Buck Jones and Tom Tyler and Hoot Gibson and especially Ken Maynard. The cards were available in those five-cent packages of gum: pink sticks, three together, covered with a sweet white powder. You couldn't blow bubbles with that particular gum, but it couldn't have mattered less. The cowboy cards were important—the pictures of those rock-faced men with eyes of blue steel.

On those windswept, leaf-tumbling afternoons we gathered after school on the sidewalk in front of Lemire's Drugstore, across from St. Jude's **Parochial School**, and we

....

parochial school a school run by a religious group

swapped and bargained and matched for the cards. Because a Ken Maynard **serial** was playing at the Globe every Saturday afternoon, he was the most popular cowboy of all, and one of his cards was worth at least ten of any other kind. Rollie Tremaine had a treasure of thirty or so, and he guarded them jealously. He'd match you for the other cards, but he risked his Ken Maynards only when the other kids threatened to leave him out of the competition altogether.

You could almost hate Rollie Tremaine. In the first place, he was the only son of Auguste Tremaine, who operated the Uptown Dry Goods Store, and he did not live in a **tenement** but in a big white birthday cake of a house on Laurel Street.

He was too fat to be effective in the football games between the Frenchtown Tigers and the North Side Knights, and he made us constantly aware of the jingle of coins in his pockets. He was able to stroll into Lemire's and casually select a quarter's worth of cowboy cards while the rest of us watched, aching with envy.

Once in a while I earned a nickel or dime by running errands or washing windows for blind old Mrs. Belander, or by finding pieces of copper, brass, and other valuable metals at the dump and selling them to the junkman. The coins clutched in my hand, I would race to Lemire's to buy

....

serial a movie shown in episodes over time
tenement an apartment building, often run-down

a cowboy card or two, hoping that Ken Maynard would stare boldly out at me as I opened the pack. At one time, before a disastrous matching session with Roger Lussier (my best friend, except where the cards were involved), I owned five Ken Maynards and considered myself a millionaire, of sorts.

One week I was particularly lucky; I had spent two afternoons washing floors for Mrs. Belander and received a quarter. Because my father had worked a full week at the shop, where a rush order for fancy combs had been received, he **allotted** my brothers and sisters and me an extra dime along with the usual ten cents for the Saturday-afternoon movie. Setting aside the movie fare, I found myself with a bonus of thirty-five cents, and I then planned to put Rollie Tremaine to shame the following Monday afternoon.

Monday was the best day to buy the cards because the candy man stopped at Lemire's every Monday morning to deliver the new **assortments**. There was nothing more exciting in the world than a fresh batch of card boxes. I rushed home from school that day and hurriedly changed my clothes, eager to set off for the store. As I burst through the doorway, letting the screen door slam behind me, my brother Armand blocked my way.

....

allotted gave
assortments collections of various things

He was fourteen, three years older than I, and a freshman at Monument High School. He had recently become a stranger to me in many ways—**indifferent to** such matters as cowboy cards and the Frenchtown Tigers— and he carried himself with a mysterious **dignity** that was **fractured** now and then when his voice began shooting off in all directions like some kind of vocal fireworks.

"Wait a minute, Jerry," he said. "I want to talk to you." He motioned me out of earshot of my mother, who was busy supervising the usual after-school **skirmish** in the kitchen.

I sighed with impatience. In recent months Armand had become a figure of authority, siding with my father and mother occasionally. As the oldest son he sometimes took advantage of his age and experience to issue rules and regulations.

"How much money have you got?" he whispered.

"You in some kind of trouble?" I asked, excitement rising in me as I remembered the blackmail plot of a movie at the Globe a month before.

He shook his head in annoyance. "Look," he said, "it's Pa's birthday tomorrow. I think we ought to chip in and buy him something…"

---

indifferent to uninterested in
dignity a quality of character that commands honor and respect
fractured broken
skirmish a minor conflict or fight

I reached into my pocket and **caressed** the coins. "Here," I said carefully, pulling out a nickel. "If we all give a nickel we should have enough to buy him something pretty nice."

He regarded me with **contempt**. "Rita already gave me fifteen cents, and I'm throwing in a quarter. Albert handed over a dime—all that's left of his birthday money. Is that all you can do—a nickel?"

"Aw, come on," I protested. "I haven't got a single Ken Maynard left, and I was going to buy some cards this afternoon."

"Ken Maynard!" he snorted. "Who's more important— him or your father?"

His question was unfair because he knew that there was no possible choice—"my father" had to be the only answer. My father was a huge man who believed in the things of the spirit, although my mother often maintained that the spirits he believed in came in bottles. He had worked at the Monument Comb Shop since the age of fourteen; his booming laugh—or grumble—greeted us each night when he returned from the factory. A steady worker when the shop had enough work, he quickened with **gaiety** on Friday nights and weekends, a bottle of beer at his elbow, and he was fond of making long speeches about the good things in life. In the middle of the Depression, for instance,

---

caressed touched gently and with affection
contempt scorn; intense disapproval
gaiety happiness; glee

he paid cash for a piano, of all things, and insisted that my twin sisters, Yolande and Yvette, take lessons once a week.

I took a dime from my pocket and handed it to Armand.

"Thanks, Jerry," he said. "I hate to take your last cent."

"That's all right," I replied, turning away and consoling myself with the thought that twenty cents was better than nothing at all.

When I arrived at Lemire's I sensed disaster in the air. Roger Lussier was kicking **disconsolately** at a tin can in the gutter, and Rollie Tremaine sat **sullenly** on the steps in front of the store.

"Save your money," Roger said. He had known about my plans to **splurge** on the cards.

"What's the matter?" I asked.

"There's no more cowboy cards," Rollie Tremaine said. "The company's not making any more."

"They're going to have president cards," Roger said, his face twisting with disgust. He pointed to the store window. "Look!"

A placard in the window announced: "Attention, Boys. Watch for the New Series. Presidents of the United States. Free in Each 5-Cent Package of Caramel Chew."

"President cards?" I asked, dismayed.

---

disconsolately unhappily; gloomily
sullenly in a glum, withdrawn, ill-tempered way
splurge spend extra

I read on: "Collect a Complete Set and Receive an Official Imitation Major League Baseball Glove, **Embossed** with Lefty Grove's Autograph."

Glove or no glove, who could become excited about presidents, of all things?

Rollie Tremaine stared at the sign. "Benjamin Harrison, for crying out loud," he said. "Why would I want Benjamin Harrison when I've got twenty-two Ken Maynards?"

I felt the warmth of guilt creep over me. I jingled the coins in my pocket, but the sound was hollow. No more Ken Maynards to buy.

"I'm going to buy a Mr. Goodbar," Rollie Tremaine decided.

I was without appetite, indifferent even to a Baby Ruth, which was my favorite. I thought of how I had betrayed Armand and, worst of all, my father.

"I'll see you after supper," I called over my shoulder to Roger as I hurried away toward home. I took the shortcut behind the church, although it involved leaping over a tall wooden fence, and I zigzagged recklessly through Mr. Thibodeau's garden, trying to outrace my guilt. I pounded up the steps and into the house, only to learn that Armand had already taken Yolande and Yvette uptown to shop for the birthday present.

....

embossed decorated with a raised design—in this case, a signature

I pedaled my bike furiously through the streets, ignoring the **indignant** horns of automobiles as I sliced through the traffic. Finally I saw Armand and my sisters emerge from the Monument Men's Shop. My heart sank when I spied the long, slim package that Armand was holding.

"Did you buy the present yet?" I asked, although I knew it was too late.

"Just now. A blue tie," Armand said. "What's the matter?"

"Nothing," I replied, my chest hurting.

He looked at me for a long moment. At first his eyes were hard, but then they softened. He smiled at me, almost sadly, and touched my arm. I turned away from him because I felt naked and exposed.

"It's all right," he said gently. "Maybe you've learned something." The words were gentle, but they held a curious dignity, the dignity remaining even when his voice suddenly cracked on the last syllable.

I wondered what was happening to me, because I did not know whether to laugh or cry.

Sister Angela was amazed when, a week before Christmas vacation, everybody in the class submitted a history essay worthy of a high mark—in some cases as high as A-minus. (Sister Angela did not believe that anyone in the world ever deserved an A.) She never learned—or at least she never let on that she knew—we all had become

....

indignant angry in response to something perceived as wrong

experts on the presidents because of the cards we purchased at Lemire's. Each card contained a picture of a president, and on the reverse side, a summary of his career. We looked at those cards so often that the biographies imprinted themselves on our minds without effort. Even our street-corner conversations were filled with such information as the fact that James Madison was called "The Father of the Constitution," or that John Adams had intended to become a minister.

The president cards were a roaring success and the cowboy cards were quickly forgotten. In the first place we did not receive gum with the cards, but a kind of chewy caramel. The caramel could be tucked into a corner of your mouth, bulging your cheek in much the same manner as wads of tobacco bulged the mouths of baseball stars. In the second place the competition for collecting the cards was fierce and frustrating—fierce because everyone was intent on being the first to send away for a baseball glove and frustrating because although there were only thirty-two presidents, including Franklin Delano Roosevelt, the variety at Lemire's was at a minimum. When the deliveryman left the boxes of cards at the store each Monday, we often discovered that one entire box was devoted to a single president—two weeks in a row the boxes contained nothing but Abraham Lincolns. One week Roger Lussier and I were the heroes of Frenchtown. We journeyed on our bicycles to the North Side, engaged three boys in a matching bout and returned with five new presidents, including Chester Alan Arthur, who up to that time had been missing.

Perhaps to sharpen our desire, the card company sent a sample glove to Mr. Lemire, and it dangled, orange and **sleek**, in the window. I was half sick with longing, thinking of my old glove at home, which I had inherited from Armand. But Rollie Tremaine's desire for the glove outdistanced my own. He even got Mr. Lemire to agree to give the glove in the window to the first person to get a complete set of cards, so that precious time wouldn't be wasted waiting for the postman.

We were delighted at Rollie Tremaine's frustration, especially since he was only a substitute player for the Tigers. Once after spending fifty cents on cards—all of which turned out to be Calvin Coolidge—he threw them to the ground, pulled some dollar bills out of his pocket and said, "The heck with it. I'm going to buy a glove!"

"Not that glove," Roger Lussier said. "Not a glove with Lefty Grove's autograph. Look what it says at the bottom of the sign."

We all looked, although we knew the words by heart: "This Glove Is Not For Sale Anywhere."

Rollie Tremaine scrambled to pick up the cards from the sidewalk, pouting more than ever. After that he was quietly **obsessed** with the presidents, hugging the cards close to his

....

sleek smooth and shiny
obsessed very focused on, to the point of being unable to think about anything else

chest and refusing to tell us how many more he needed to complete his set.

I too was obsessed with the cards, because they had become things of comfort in a world that had suddenly grown **dismal**. After Christmas a **layoff** at the shop had thrown my father out of work. He received no paycheck for four weeks, and the only income we had was from Armand's after-school job at the Blue and White Grocery Store—a job he lost finally when business **dwindled** as the layoff continued.

Although we had enough food and clothing—my father's credit had always been good, a matter of pride with him—the inactivity made my father restless and irritable. He did not drink any beer at all, and laughed loudly, but not convincingly, after gulping down a glass of water and saying, "Lent came early this year." The twins fell sick and went to the hospital to have their tonsils removed. My father was confident that he would return to work eventually and pay off his debts, but he seemed to age before our eyes.

When orders again were received at the comb shop and he returned to work, another disaster occurred, although I was the only one aware of it. Armand fell in love.

------

dismal gloomy; bleak; sad
layoff a situation when employees are released from their jobs, usually for a limited time
dwindled decreased; lessened

I discovered his situation by accident, when I happened to pick up a piece of paper that had fallen to the floor in the bedroom he and I shared. I frowned at the paper, puzzled.

"Dear Sally, When I look into your eyes the world stands still …"

The letter was snatched from my hands before I finished reading it.

"What's the big idea, snooping around?" Armand asked, his face **crimson**. "Can't a guy have any privacy?"

He had never mentioned privacy before. "It was on the floor," I said. "I didn't know it was a letter. Who's Sally?"

He flung himself across the bed. "You tell anybody and I'll **muckalize** you," he threatened. "Sally Knowlton."

Nobody in Frenchtown had a name like Knowlton.

"A girl from the North Side?" I asked, **incredulous**. He rolled over and faced me, anger in his eyes, and a kind of despair, too.

"What's the matter with that? Think she's too good for me?" he asked. "I'm warning you, Jerry, if you tell anybody …"

"Don't worry," I said. Love had no particular place in my life; it seemed an unnecessary waste of time. And

---

crimson deep red
muckalize a made-up word meaning "make into muck or mud"
incredulous unable to believe

a girl from the North Side was so **remote** that for all practical purposes she did not exist. But I was curious. "What are you writing her a letter for? Did she leave town, or something?"

"She hasn't left town," he answered. "I wasn't going to send it. I just felt like writing to her."

I was glad that I had never become involved with love—love that brought desperation to your eyes, that caused you to write letters you did not plan to send. Shrugging with indifference, I began to search in the closet for the old baseball glove. I found it on the shelf, under some old sneakers. The webbing was torn and the padding gone. I thought of the sting I would feel when a sharp grounder slapped into the glove, and I **winced**.

"You tell anybody about me and Sally and I'll—"

"I know. You'll muckalize me."

I did not **divulge** his secret and often shared his agony, particularly when he sat at the supper table and left my mother's special butterscotch pie untouched. I had never realized before how terrible love could be. But my compassion was short-lived because I had other things to worry about: report cards due at Eastertime; the loss of income from old Mrs. Belander, who had gone to live with a daughter in Boston; and, of course, the presidents.

....

remote distant; far away
winced flinched; made a pained expression
divulge to tell; to reveal

Because a **stalemate** had been reached, the president cards were the **dominant** force in our lives—mine, Roger Lussier's, and Rollie Tremaine's. For three weeks, as the baseball season approached, each of us had a complete set—complete except for one president, Grover Cleveland. Each time a box of cards arrived at the store we hurriedly bought them (as hurriedly as our funds allowed) and tore off the wrappers, only to be confronted by James Monroe or Martin Van Buren or someone else. But never Grover Cleveland, never the man who had been the twenty-second and the twenty-fourth president of the United States. We argued about Grover Cleveland. Should he be placed between Chester Alan Arthur and Benjamin Harrison as the twenty-second president or did he belong between Benjamin Harrison and William McKinley as the twenty-fourth president? Was the card company playing fair? Roger Lussier brought up a horrifying possibility—did we need two Grover Clevelands to complete the set?

Indignant, we stormed Lemire's and protested to the **harassed** storeowner, who had long since **vowed** never to stock a new series. Muttering angrily, he searched his bills and receipts for a list of rules.

---

stalemate point at which nothing further can be done because two sides cannot agree
dominant most important; controlling
harassed constantly bothered
vowed promised

"All right," he announced. "Says here you only need one Grover Cleveland to finish the set. Now get out, all of you, unless you've got money to spend."

Outside the store, Rollie Tremaine picked up an empty tobacco tin and scaled it across the street. "Boy," he said. "I'd give five dollars for a Grover Cleveland."

When I returned home I found Armand sitting on the **piazza** steps, his chin in his hands. His mood of **dejection** mirrored my own, and I sat down beside him. We did not say anything for a while.

"Want to throw the ball around?" I asked.

He sighed, not bothering to answer.

"You sick?" I asked.

He stood up and hitched up his trousers, pulled at his ear and finally told me what the matter was—there was a big dance next week at the high school, the Spring Promenade, and Sally had asked him to be her **escort**.

I shook my head at the **folly** of love. "Well, what's so bad about that?"

"How can I take Sally to a fancy dance?" he asked desperately. "I'd have to buy her a **corsage**…And my shoes are practically falling apart. Pa's got too many worries now to buy me new shoes or give me money for flowers for a girl."

piazza porch
dejection deep sadness; gloom
escort date or companion
folly foolishness
corsage flowers worn on the shoulder or wrist on a special occasion

I nodded in sympathy. "Yeah," I said. "Look at me. Baseball time is almost here, and all I've got is that old glove. And no Grover Cleveland card yet..."

"Grover Cleveland?" he asked. "They've got some of those up on the North Side. Some kid was telling me there's a store that's got them. He says they're looking for Warren G. Harding."

"Holy smoke!" I said. "I've got an extra Warren G. Harding!" Pure joy sang in my veins. I ran to my bicycle, swung into the seat—and found that the front tire was flat.

"I'll help you fix it," Armand said.

Within half an hour I was at the North Side Drugstore, where several boys were matching cards on the sidewalk. Silently but blissfully I shouted: President Grover Cleveland, here I come!

After Armand had left for the dance, all dressed up as if it were Sunday, the small green box containing the corsage under his arm, I sat on the railing of the piazza, letting my feet dangle. The neighborhood was quiet because the Frenchtown Tigers were at Daggett's Field, practicing for the first baseball game of the season.

I thought of Armand and the ridiculous expression on his face when he'd stood before the mirror in the bedroom. I'd avoided looking at his new black shoes. "Love," I muttered.

Spring had arrived in a sudden stampede of apple blossoms and fragrant breezes. Windows had been thrown open and dust mops had banged on the sills all day long as the women busied themselves with housecleaning. I was puzzled by my **lethargy**. Wasn't spring supposed to make everything bright and gay?

I turned at the sound of footsteps on the stairs. Roger Lussier greeted me with a sour face.

"I thought you were practicing with the Tigers," I said.

"Rollie Tremaine," he said. "I just couldn't stand him." He slammed his fist against the railing. "Jeez, why did he have to be the one to get a Grover Cleveland? You should see him showing off. He won't let anybody even touch that glove..."

I felt like Benedict Arnold and knew that I had to confess what I had done.

"Roger," I said, "I got a Grover Cleveland card up on the North Side. I sold it to Rollie Tremaine for five dollars."

"Are you crazy?" he asked.

"I needed that five dollars. It was an—an emergency."

"Boy!" he said, looking down at the ground and shaking his head. "What did you have to do a thing like that for?"

I watched him as he turned away and began walking down the stairs.

"Hey, Roger!" I called.

....

lethargy extreme drowsiness

He squinted up at me as if I were a stranger, someone he'd never seen before.

"What?" he asked, his voice flat.

"I had to do it," I said. "Honest."

He didn't answer. He headed toward the fence, searching for the board we had loosened to give us a secret passage.

I thought of my father and Armand and Rollie Tremaine and Grover Cleveland and wished that I could go away someplace far away. But there was no place to go.

Roger found the loose slat in the fence and slipped through. I felt betrayed: weren't you supposed to feel good when you did something fine and noble?

A moment later two hands gripped the top of the fence and Roger's face appeared. "Was it a real emergency?" he yelled.

"A real one!" I called. "Something important!"

His face dropped from sight and his voice reached me across the yard: "All right."

"See you tomorrow!" I yelled.

I swung my legs over the railing again. The gathering dusk began to soften the sharp edges of the fence, the roof tops, the distant church steeple. I sat there a long time, waiting for the good feeling to come. ❖

My Father Is a Simple Man

by Luis Omar Salinas

I walk to town with my father
to buy a newspaper. He walks slower
than I do so I must slow up.
The street is filled with children.
We argue about the price
of **pomegranates**, I convince
him it is the fruit of **scholars**.
He has taken me on this journey
and it's been lifelong.
He's sure I'll be healthy
so long as I eat more oranges
and tells me the orange
has seeds and so is **perpetual**;
and we too will come back
like the orange trees.
I ask him what he thinks
about death and he says
he will gladly face it when
it comes but won't jump
out in front of a car.

....

pomegranates tart, juicy, red fruit with many seeds
scholars learned people devoted to study
perpetual ongoing; everlasting; continuing forever

I'd gladly give my life
for this man with a sixth
grade education, whose kindness
and patience are true …
The truth of it is, he's the scholar,
and when the bitter-hard reality
comes at me like a punishing
evil stranger, I can always
remember that here was a man
who was a worker and provider,
who learned the simple facts
in life and lived by them,
who held no **pretense**.
And when he leaves without
benefit of **fanfare** or applause
I shall have learned what little
there is about greatness. ❖

pretense false appearance or intention
fanfare a musical salute with trumpets; or, a showy
public display

Raymond's Run

by Toni Cade Bambara

I don't have much work to do around the house like some girls. My mother does that. And I don't have to earn my pocket money by hustling; George runs errands for the big boys and sells Christmas cards. And anything else that's got to get done, my father does. All I have to do in life is **mind** my brother Raymond, which is enough.

Sometimes I slip and say my little brother Raymond. But as any fool can see he's much bigger and he's older too. But a lot of people call him my little brother cause he needs looking after cause he's not quite right. And a lot of smart mouths got lots to say about that too, especially when George was minding him. But now, if anybody has anything to say to Raymond, anything to say about his big head, they have to come by me. And I don't **play the dozens** or believe in standing around with somebody in my face doing a lot of talking. I much rather just knock you down and take my chances even if I am a little girl with skinny arms and a squeaky voice, which is how I got the name Squeaky. And if things get too rough, I run. And as anybody can tell you, I'm the fastest thing on two feet.

....

mind to look after; to take care of
play the dozens to engage in an exchange of insults, teasing, or taunting

There is no track meet that I don't win the first place medal. I used to win the twenty-yard dash when I was a little kid in kindergarten. Nowadays, it's the fifty-yard dash. And tomorrow I'm subject to run the quarter-meter relay all by myself and come in first, second, and third. The big kids call me **Mercury** cause I'm the swiftest thing in the neighborhood. Everybody knows that—except two people who know better, my father and me. He can beat me to Amsterdam Avenue with me having a two fire-hydrant headstart and him running with his hands in his pockets and whistling. But that's private information. Cause you can imagine some thirty-five-year-old man stuffing himself into PAL shorts to race little kids? So as far as everyone's concerned, I'm the fastest and that goes for Gretchen, too, who has put out the tale that she is going to win the first-place medal this year. Ridiculous. In the second place, she's got short legs. In the third place, she's got freckles. In the first place, no one can beat me and that's all there is to it.

I'm standing on the corner admiring the weather and about to take a stroll down Broadway so I can practice my breathing exercises, and I've got Raymond walking on the inside close to the buildings, cause he's subject to fits of fantasy and starts thinking he's a circus performer and that the curb is a tightrope strung high in the air.

Mercury in ancient Roman mythology, the messenger god, known for speed

And sometimes after a rain he likes to step down off his tightrope right into the gutter and slosh around getting his shoes and cuffs wet. Then I get hit when I get home. Or sometimes if you don't watch him he'll dash across traffic to the island in the middle of Broadway and give the pigeons a fit. Then I have to go behind him apologizing to all the old people sitting around trying to get some sun and getting all upset with the pigeons fluttering around them, scattering their newspapers and upsetting the waxpaper lunches in their laps. So I keep Raymond on the inside of me, and he plays like he's driving a stage coach which is O.K. by me so long as he doesn't run me over or interrupt my breathing exercises, which I have to do on account of I'm serious about my running, and I don't care who knows it.

Now some people like to act like things come easy to them, won't let on that they practice. Not me. I'll high-prance down 34th Street like a rodeo pony to keep my knees strong even if it does get my mother uptight so that she walks ahead like she's not with me, don't know me, is all by herself on a shopping trip, and I am somebody else's crazy child. Now you take Cynthia Procter for instance. She's just the opposite. If there's a test tomorrow, she'll say something like, "Oh, I guess I'll play handball this afternoon and watch television tonight," just to let you know she ain't thinking about the test. Or like last week when she won the spelling bee for the millionth time,

"A good thing you got 'receive,' Squeaky, cause I would have got it wrong. I completely forgot about the spelling bee." And she'll clutch the lace on her blouse like it was a narrow escape. Oh, brother. But of course when I pass her house on my early morning trots around the block, she is practicing the scales on the piano over and over and over and over. Then in music class she always lets herself get bumped around so she falls **accidently** on purpose onto the piano stool and is so surprised to find herself sitting there that she decides just for fun to try out the **ole** keys. And what do you know—**Chopin**'s waltzes just spring out of her fingertips and she's the most surprised thing in the world. A regular **prodigy**. I could kill people like that. I stay up all night studying the words for the spelling bee. And you can see me any time of day practicing running. I never walk if I can trot, and shame on Raymond if he can't keep up. But of course he does, cause if he hangs back someone's **liable** to walk up to him and get smart, or take his allowance from him, or ask him where he got that great big pumpkin head. People are so stupid sometimes.

So I'm strolling down Broadway breathing out and breathing in on counts of seven, which is my lucky number,

....

accidently an intentional misspelling of *accidentally*, to capture the character's casual way of speaking
ole old
Chopin Polish composer and pianist of the 19th century, famed for his works for piano
prodigy genius; someone with amazing ability
liable likely

and here comes Gretchen and her sidekicks: Mary Louise, who used to be a friend of mine when she first moved to Harlem from Baltimore and got beat up by everybody till I took up for her on account of her mother and my mother used to sing in the same choir when they were young girls, but people ain't grateful, so now she hangs out with the new girl Gretchen and talks about me like a dog; and Rosie, who is as fat as I am skinny and has a big mouth where Raymond is concerned and is too stupid to know that there is not a big deal of difference between herself and Raymond and that she can't afford to throw stones. So they are steady coming up Broadway and I see right away that it's going to be one of those Dodge City scenes cause the street ain't that big and they're close to the buildings just as we are. First I think I'll step into the candy store and look over the new comics and let them pass. But that's chicken and I've got a reputation to consider. So then I think I'll just walk straight on through them or even over them if necessary. But as they get to me, they slow down. I'm ready to fight, cause like I said I don't feature a whole lot of chit-chat, I much prefer to just knock you down right from the jump and save everybody a lotta precious time.

"You signing up for the May Day races?" smiles Mary Louise, only it's not a smile at all. A dumb question like that doesn't deserve an answer. Besides, there's just me and Gretchen standing there really, so no use wasting my breath talking to shadows.

"I don't think you're going to win this time," says Rosie, trying to signify with her hands on her hips all salty, completely forgetting that I have whupped her behind many times for less salt than that.

"I always win cause I'm the best," I say straight at Gretchen who is, as far as I'm concerned, the only one talking in this **ventriloquist-dummy routine**. Gretchen smiles, but it's not a smile, and I'm thinking that girls never really smile at each other because they don't know how and don't want to know how and there's probably no one to teach us how, cause grown-up girls don't know either. Then they all look at Raymond who has just brought his mule team to a standstill. And they're about to see what trouble they can get into through him.

"What grade you in now, Raymond?"

"You got anything to say to my brother, you say it to me, Mary Louise Williams of Raggedy Town, Baltimore."

"What are you, his mother?" **sasses** Rosie.

"That's right, Fatso. And the next word out of anybody and I'll be their mother too." So they just stand there and Gretchen shifts from one leg to the other and so do they. Then Gretchen puts her hands on her hips and is about to say something with her freckle-face self but doesn't. Then she walks around me looking me up and down but keeps

....

ventriloquist-dummy routine a performance in which the ventriloquist, a person who speaks with little or no lip movement, makes it appear that the dummy, or puppet, is speaking
sasses talks disrespectfully

walking up Broadway, and her sidekicks follow her. So me and Raymond smile at each other and he says, "Gidyap" to his team and I continue with my breathing exercises, strolling down Broadway toward the ice man on 145th with not a care in the world cause I am Miss Quicksilver herself.

I take my time getting to the park on May Day because the track meet is the last thing on the program. The biggest thing on the program is the May Pole dancing, which I can do without, thank you, even if my mother thinks it's a shame I don't take part and act like a girl for a change. You'd think my mother'd be grateful not to have to make me a white **organdy** dress with a big satin sash and buy me new white baby-doll shoes that can't be taken out of the box till the big day. You'd think she'd be glad her daughter ain't out there prancing around a May Pole getting the new clothes all dirty and sweaty and trying to act like a fairy or a flower or whatever you're supposed to be when you should be trying to be yourself, whatever that is, which is, as far as I am concerned, a poor Black girl who really can't afford to buy shoes and a new dress you only wear once a lifetime cause it won't fit next year.

I was once a strawberry in a Hansel and Gretel pageant when I was in nursery school and didn't have no better sense than to dance on tiptoe with my arms in a circle over my head doing umbrella steps and being a perfect fool just so my mother and father could come dressed up and clap.

....

organdy a fine, stiff, almost see-through fabric

You'd think they'd know better than to encourage that kind of nonsense. I am not a strawberry. I do not dance on my toes. I run. That is what I am all about. So I always come late to the May Day program, just in time to get my number pinned on and lay in the grass till they announce the fifty-yard dash.

I put Raymond in the little swings, which is a tight squeeze this year and will be impossible next year. Then I look around for Mr. Pearson, who pins the numbers on. I'm really looking for Gretchen if you want to know the truth, but she's not around. The park is jam-packed. Parents in hats and corsages and breast-pocket handkerchiefs peeking up. Kids in white dresses and light-blue suits. The **parkees** unfolding chairs and chasing the rowdy kids from Lenox as if they had no right to be there. The big guys with their caps on backwards, leaning against the fence swirling the basketballs on the tips of their fingers, waiting for all these crazy people to clear out the park so they can play. Most of the kids in my class are carrying bass drums and **glockenspiels** and flutes. You'd think they'd put in a few bongos or something for real like that.

Then here comes Mr. Pearson with his clipboard and his cards and pencils and whistles and safety pins and fifty million other things he's always dropping all over the place with his clumsy self. He sticks out in a crowd because he's

---

parkees slang for people who work or spend much time in the park
glockenspiels instruments with metal bars, played with small, light hammers

on stilts. We used to call him Jack and the Beanstalk to get him mad. But I'm the only one that can outrun him and get away, and I'm too grown for that silliness now.

"Well, Squeaky," he says, checking my name off the list and handing me number seven and two pins. And I'm thinking he's got no right to call me Squeaky, if I can't call him Beanstalk.

"Hazel Elizabeth Deborah Parker," I correct him and tell him to write it down on his board.

"Well, Hazel Elizabeth Deborah Parker, going to give someone else a break this year?" I squint at him real hard to see if he is seriously thinking I should lose the race on purpose just to give someone else a break. "Only six girls running this time," he continues, shaking his head sadly like it's my fault all of New York didn't turn out in sneakers.

"That new girl should give you a run for your money." He looks around the park for Gretchen like a **periscope** in a submarine movie. "Wouldn't it be a nice gesture if you were…to ahhh…"

I give him such a look he couldn't finish putting that idea into words. Grownups got a lot of nerve sometimes. I pin number seven to myself and stomp away, I'm so burnt. And I go straight for the track and stretch out on the grass while the band winds up with "Oh, the Monkey Wrapped His Tail Around the Flag Pole," which my teacher calls by

---

periscope a tube-like instrument used to see things not in one's direct line of sight

some other name. The man on the loudspeaker is calling everyone over to the track and I'm on my back looking at the sky, trying to pretend I'm in the country, but I can't, because even grass in the city feels hard as sidewalk, and there's just no pretending you are anywhere but in a "concrete jungle" as my grandfather says.

The twenty-yard dash takes all of two minutes cause most of the little kids don't know no better than to run off the track or run the wrong way or run smack into the fence and fall down and cry. One little kid, though, has got the good sense to run straight for the white ribbon up ahead so he wins. Then the second-graders line up for the thirty-yard dash and I don't even bother to turn my head to watch cause Raphael Perez always wins. He wins before he even begins by **psyching** the runners, telling them they're going to trip on their shoelaces and fall on their faces or lose their shorts or something, which he doesn't really have to do since he is very fast, almost as fast as I am. After that is the forty-yard dash which I use to run when I was in first grade. Raymond is hollering from the swings cause he knows I'm about to do my thing cause the man on the loudspeaker has just announced the fifty-yard dash, although he might just as well be giving a recipe for angel food cake cause you can hardly make out what he's sayin for the static. I get up and slip off my sweat pants and then

....

psyching slang for "intimidating," "scaring," or "tricking"

I see Gretchen standing at the starting line, kicking her legs out like a pro. Then as I get into place I see that ole Raymond is on line on the other side of the fence, bending down with his fingers on the ground just like he knew what he was doing. I was going to yell at him but then I didn't. It burns up your energy to holler.

Every time, just before I take off in a race, I always feel like I'm in a dream, the kind of dream you have when you're sick with fever and feel all hot and weightless. I dream I'm flying over a sandy beach in the early morning sun, kissing the leaves of the trees as I fly by. And there's always the smell of apples, just like in the country when I was little and used to think I was a choo-choo train, running through the fields of corn and chugging up the hill to the orchard. And all the time I'm dreaming this, I get lighter and lighter until I'm flying over the beach again, getting blown through the sky like a feather that weighs nothing at all. But once I spread my fingers in the dirt and crouch over the Get on Your Mark, the dream goes and I am solid again and am telling myself, Squeaky you must win, you must win, you are the fastest thing in the world, you can even beat your father up Amsterdam if you really try. And then I feel my weight coming back just behind my knees then down to my feet then into the earth and the pistol shot explodes in my blood and I am off and weightless again, flying past the other runners, my arms pumping up and down and the whole world is quiet except for the crunch as I zoom over the gravel in the track. I glance to my left and there is no one. To the right, a blurred Gretchen, who's got her chin jutting out as if it would win the race all by itself. And on the other side of the fence is Raymond with his arms down to his side and the palms tucked up behind him, running in his very own style, and it's the first time I ever saw that and I almost stop to watch my brother Raymond on his first run. But the white ribbon is bouncing toward me and I tear past it, racing into the distance till my feet with a mind of their own start digging up footfuls of dirt and brake me short. Then all the kids standing on the side pile on me, banging me on the back and slapping my head with their May Day programs, for I have won again and everybody on 151st Street can walk tall for another year.

"In first place ..." the man on the loudspeaker is clear as a bell now. But then he pauses and the loudspeaker starts to whine. Then static. And I lean down to catch my breath and here comes Gretchen walking back, for she's overshot the finish line too, huffing and puffing with her hands on her hips taking it slow, breathing in steady time like a real pro and I sort of like her a little for the first time. "In first place—" and then three or four voices get all mixed up on the loudspeaker and I dig my sneaker into the grass and stare at Gretchen who's staring back, we both wondering just who did win.

I can hear old Beanstalk arguing with the man on the loudspeaker and then a few others running their mouths about what the stopwatches say. Then I hear Raymond yanking at the fence to call me and I wave to **shush** him, but he keeps rattling the fence like a gorilla in a cage like in them gorilla movies, but then like a dancer or something he starts climbing up nice and easy but very fast. And it occurs to me, watching how smoothly he climbs hand over hand and remembering how he looked running with his arms down to his side and with the wind pulling his mouth back and his teeth showing and all, it occurred to me that Raymond would make a very fine runner. Doesn't he always keep up with me on my trots? And he surely knows how to breathe in counts of seven cause he's always doing it at the dinner table, which drives my brother George up the wall. And I'm smiling to beat the band cause if I've lost this race, or if me and Gretchen tied, or even if I've won, I can always retire as a runner and begin a whole new career as a coach with Raymond as my champion. After all, with a little more study I can beat Cynthia and her phony self at the spelling bee. And if I bugged my mother, I could get piano lessons and become a star. And I have a big **rep** as the **baddest** thing around. And I've got a roomful of

shush quiet
rep short for "reputation"
baddest slang for "best"

ribbons and medals and awards. But what has Raymond got to call his own?

So I stand there with my new plans, laughing out loud by this time as Raymond jumps down from the fence and runs over with his teeth showing and his arms down to the side, which no one before him has quite mastered as a running style. And by the time he comes over I'm jumping up and down so glad to see him—my brother Raymond, a great runner in the family tradition. But of course everyone thinks I'm jumping up and down because the men on the loudspeaker have finally gotten themselves together and compared notes and are announcing "In first place—Miss Hazel Elizabeth Deborah Parker." (Dig that.) "In second place—Miss Gretchen P. Lewis." And I look over at Gretchen wondering what the "P" stands for. And I smile. Cause she's good, no doubt about it. Maybe she'd like to help me coach Raymond; she obviously is serious about running, as any fool can see. And she nods to congratulate me and then she smiles. And I smile. We stand there with this big smile of respect between us. It's about as real a smile as girls can do for each other, considering we don't practice real smiling every day, you know, cause maybe we too busy being flowers or fairies or strawberries instead of something honest and worthy of respect...you know...like being people. ❖

Saving Tobe

from Sweet Hope
by Mary Bucci Bush

Tobe motioned for Osvaldo to follow him closer to
the river's edge. Sand ripples showed underneath the
water until, a yard from shore, the bottom disappeared
into murkiness.

The sandbar was five feet wide and nearly fifteen feet
long, an easy target. Tobe's stones hit the edge of the
bar, but Osvaldo's always splashed short. Soon they were
panting from the exertion. Tobe poked his toes into the
water. Osvaldo took off his shoes and stood beside Tobe,
the cool water tickling his feet.

Tobe told Osvaldo how a whole steamship with hundreds of people on board was sitting at the river bottom right there where he was pointing. He repeated words for Osvaldo to say: "river," "gold," "pirates."

The river flowed steadfastly past them. Ocean waves pushed a shell or a clump of weeds onto the shore, then sucked it out, then threw it back on shore again. But whatever this river took did not come back.

"Go on," Tobe encouraged him, knowing the dangers of playing in the forbidden river. "Go swim." He pointed to the sandbar. "Swim on out to the sandbar." He motioned to his waist, assuring Osvaldo that the water was only that deep. Tobe found a stick, then poked it into the water as far in front of him as he could reach. "See? Ain't even deep," he said.

They were standing in the shallow water to their ankles, whipping the stick in the water and stirring up the muddy bottom while the woods behind them **thrummed** with insects and birdsong. "Big ol' giant fish live out in the deep middle," Tobe said. "He jump up one time, swallow a whole river boat, all one gulp." He squatted down, so low that water lapped at his rear end.

Then they were both sitting in the water. Tobe flung off his ragged shirt. They leaned back on their elbows and let their legs float, the current swaying them toward the landing.

....

thrummed made a soft continuous humming sound

Osvaldo heard a sound, like branches moving or someone walking, coming from the woods behind them, above the sound of the river. He touched Tobe's arm, and motioned for him to listen. But no parents emerged, no sisters. It gave Osvaldo a creepy feeling, as if the woods were alive and had eyes.

A great white bird rose up from the grassy shore nearby and flapped across the water, pulling its long dark legs in close to its body, its bulky wings almost dipping into the water as it skimmed the surface. And then the bird rose higher, stretched its crooked neck, made a graceful swooping turn and landed farther down near the shore.

Osvaldo asked Tobe if he'd seen the bird, but Tobe merely flopped onto his stomach and rested his chin in his hands, his legs floating behind him. Water licked at his face and he laughed and raised his chin. He had done this only once before, alone, but now with another boy beside him it was as if he had always played in the river.

Then a turtle floated by, and the boys waded in water to their knees to retrieve it.

Now that Tobe was in the water and his feet were still touching bottom, all the warnings he had heard about playing in the river vanished. It wasn't until his foot slipped and he felt his leg dropping, and then his body following, that something woke in him. He thrashed his arms and screamed for help.

Osvaldo took a step toward him, and then stopped. Tobe churned his arms toward shore as the current pulled him slowly in the opposite direction. His mouth opened and shut as he tried to cry out for help while spitting to keep the water from choking him.

Osvaldo turned toward the trees. "*Aiuto!*" he shouted. "*Aiuto!*" He turned back and shouted in Italian for Tobe to swim, and he tried to reach an arm out to him. Finally he ran for the stick the boy had been playing with and called for Tobe to grab it, but the stick was ridiculously short. All the while Tobe's panicked eyes stayed on Osvaldo. His face bobbed farther out in the water, so that he looked like a flower, a dark floating blossom. Osvaldo stared mutely at the bobbing flower, then took off running for the trees.

Their dinner break was nearly over when Fancy Hall and Amalia Pascala each looked up, their noses raised as if catching something in the air. Their eyes moved slowly over the children and adults sprawled around them, and their ears listened, although neither of them knew in those moments what they were listening for. Their eyes met briefly as they rose to their feet. By the time they were standing, what their bodies had unknowingly sensed turned to sudden consciousness. Within seconds the entire group was running into the woods, calling for the boys.

They broke through the trees onto the sandy clearing at the same time Osvaldo leaped from the sand into the scrub oaks, shouting incoherently. Step Hall reached out as if to steady himself and caught the boy by the arm. For a moment Osvaldo dangled in mid-air while a dozen pairs of startled eyes watched his churning feet, the great river flowing behind him. Then Step dropped the boy and they ran for the river.

Fancy screamed when she saw her son slapping at the water, a dull, exhausted look on his face. He had already been carried another twenty feet downstream and farther away from shore.

Step splashed into the water while his wife followed, her arms stretched toward the boy. The others grabbed her skirt to keep her from throwing herself into the river. Step's foot slipped at a drop-off, and he plunged into water to his waist. He struggled against the current to keep his footing. Someone called for a rope, and the scrawny old man ran back to the wagons. Another man cursed himself for not bringing a rope when they had first run into the woods. Where else would young boys be, after all, than in the river where they weren't supposed to be?

As if on cue, the black Americans joined hands, making a chain of their bodies that allowed Step to venture farther into the water. The Italians added their own bodies as links in the chain. But the water became too deep and the current too strong. "Daddy," Tobe gasped as the river tugged at him. The distance widened between them.

Amalia pulled Osvaldo close and called the girls to her side. "Pray for the little boy," she told them.

Serafin waded into the water, holding onto the outstretched arms until he reached Step Hall, the shouting and crying close in his ears. He grabbed Step's arm and leaned over the river, reaching for Tobe as if **beckoning** him from the water. The motion jarred him: once again he was touching his brother Valerio's hand. He held the fingers for a moment, and then Valerio disappeared.

He let go of Step Hall. His feet touched bottom for just a moment before the current lifted him and he started swimming.

"Fool, Serafin!" Amalia shrieked. "Come back."

Osvaldo watched in horror as his father was carried away. "Daddy," he cried out. "Where are you going?" He knew he was the cause of this. "*Mi scusa,*" Osvaldo cried.

Serafin had seen foolish young men who thought they could fight the sea and win—a dangerous attitude for a fisherman to have. He never thought of himself as such a man, but now he felt his anger against the river rising, and he tried to calm it. It was the anger that killed you.

It was easy to reach the boy, as he knew it would be. Returning would be another matter. Tobe turned his eyes to Serafin like a baby waking from sleep. "*Stai bene,*" Serafin told him. "You're going to be okay." He slipped his arm

beckoning calling

under Tobe's, lifting him in the water so that he could breathe. Tobe whimpered.

The water cradled Serafin and the boy as they held each other. Then Serafin turned his head sharply, to see how far he had drifted from shore, and the sight shocked him. I may as well be in the middle of the ocean, he thought.

The water felt surprisingly cold now. It tugged at his legs, and for a moment he kicked out violently, thinking he had become snagged in something, but it was only the current playing tricks on him. He plowed the water with his right arm while he fought to keep the boy above water with the other. He heard nothing from shore, but he saw the tense, frightened faces watching him, the way he had watched twice from his boat. The cold water made his legs feel heavy and sluggish. The boy was weightless beside him, an empty burlap sack. *"Stai bene?"* he called out, his lips brushing the boy's cheek like a kiss. There was no answer, just a slight movement, perhaps the splash of a hand.

His arm ached. He wondered how such a small child had been able to swim against the current for so long. He told himself to try not to think about the pain and the distance between himself and shore. It would have been hard enough to swim with both arms, but this way, holding onto the boy, it seemed impossible. Just one more stroke. One more and then another and then another.

Lazzaro waved his arms at Serafin as the group followed him slowly downstream. "Be strong," Lazzaro shouted. "Don't give up." Suddenly Serafin was afraid. It was as if the river had stopped for a moment and he could see everything clearly. It had not crossed his mind when he stepped into the water that he might not come out alive. Now he saw the terrified looks on his wife and children and best friend.

"Don't give up, hold on," Lazzaro called, and Serafin was stunned to realize he was drowning. What would happen to his wife and children? How could he leave them alone in the hell he had brought them to, with the pain of his death to further burden them? Visiting him at Hyner cemetery, where the rest of the godforsaken Italians lay.

A black man waded into the water, extending a rope to Serafin, then letting it drop when he saw that a rope was useless. "Come on," Lazzaro shouted. "Just a little more." Serafin blinked his eyes hard, trying to clear the water from them, and he was surprised a second time to realize he had actually inched himself closer to shore, even though the current carried him downstream. Just his fate, he thought, to die like this, not a mule's length from being saved.

The group formed a human chain again and eased into deeper water. Serafin found himself looking into the face of Step Hall, who held the rope. They were shouting at him and at each other, but a rushing sound filled his ears, and he could not make out their words. Step leaned into the river while the others held him. His face tensed, the eyes narrowed as he studied Serafin's face with the look of someone backed into a corner and **gauging** his last desperate move. Then Step Hall tossed the loop of rope with his one free hand. Serafin watched its slow flight in the air; it seemed to hang suspended in front of his eyes before plopping gently in the water a few feet in front of him. Several times Step pulled in the noose, then tossed it out again. Finally he stopped and cursed himself, fretting over the rope as if searching for the flaw in it. Then he leaned forward once more, set a steady gaze on Serafin's face and let go the rope. It sailed before Serafin's eyes for a moment—a fleeting shadow, a leaf blowing in the wind— before floating down over his head. Step let out a quick, triumphant shout, then pulled, and Serafin felt the pressure against the back of his neck. He raised his head in the water and arched his neck to keep the rope from slipping off. And then Step reached out, snagged Serafin's hand and pulled him in.

Step and Fancy Hall snatched their son from Serafin as he collapsed on his knees ashore. He felt the air heave around him, like a gust blowing in and out of a room. It was his family gathering at his side. And then there came a barely **discernible** touch, Amalia's hand on his arm, removing the rope from his neck.

----

gauging measuring
discernible noticeable

Serafin noticed in the same hazy way the commotion a short distance from him, Fancy Hall crying and rocking her son as the others pried the boy out of her hands and laid him on the grass. Step slapped at his son and shook him saying, "Come on boy, come on boy" through gritted teeth until finally the boy coughed and vomited. Fancy touched Tobe's face, his chest, his arms. "Did you ever think?" she cried. "Oh Lord, did you ever think?"

Amalia slapped Serafin across the face with such force that he fell sideways.

"What the hell did you think you were doing going out there, leaving us?" she screamed at him. "I know your men die in water!"

"*Dio santo*," Fiorenza said, pulling her away. Amalia cursed Serafin, beating at his face while Fiorenza struggled to hold her back. Lazzaro pinned Amalia's arms to her sides until they went still and she began sobbing.

Serafin righted himself on his knees, taking his children's hands for support. "It's okay," he tried to say, but what came out sounded like he was attempting to clear his throat. He knelt for a minute, catching his breath, waiting for the feeling in his arm to return.

"You okay?" Lazzaro asked.

His wife and children stared at him mutely, their silence more painful than anything his muscles had felt in the water.

"Let me breathe," Serafin told them.

And Tobe was a newborn calf a few yards away, trembling and skinny and slick with water. His father helped him to his feet, but the boy's legs gave way and he sprawled on the ground, looking up at them with bewildered eyes.

Step put his hand on the boy's head. "Lay still now," he told him. "Let your strength come back." One of the men took off his shirt and laid it over Tobe's chest.

Serafin felt his hands stinging now, from the water drying in the cuts he had gotten from baling hay. Pale, bloated lines crisscrossed his palms, the whitened edges of the cuts like the mouths of dead fish.

He was there, all over again, four years ago, looking into Valerio's white, stone face as he lay dripping in the bottom of the boat. That awful understanding: his brother was dead. It was final; there was no changing it. If they had pulled him out of the water two minutes sooner, one minute, who knows?

Serafin had left in the dark morning as usual, taking Valerio along as he sometimes did. They had slipped out into deep water with Valerio talking about a girl he had met on the *via Villanova*, how he had walked with her all the way down to the sea and had gotten up the courage to kiss her just when she bent over to pick up a piece of driftwood. "I was kissing the air," he laughed. Talking, talking, always talking. They had gone out in his boat with

Valerio talking and returned three hours later with Valerio dead. There was no way to explain the anguish. Valerio was no more.

Serafin knelt at the riverbank clutching his stomach, sobbing.

And yet the boy, Tobe Hall, was saved. Wonder mingled with grief, astonishment as heavy as grief, and painful, too, an astonishing, beautiful pain impossible to comprehend.

Valerio, after four years dead, you have come back to us?

The others watched uneasily. Step Hall's jaw tightened as he waited to see what would happen.

"It's okay," Lazzaro told Serafin. He tried to take the man by his shoulders, raise him to his feet, but Serafin could not be moved. "Everything's all right now, my friend," he told Serafin in a gentle, coaxing voice.

Lazzaro and Fiorenza exchanged glances with Amalia. It had been a while since they had seen Serafin like this. Amalia had been on the verge of telling Fiorenza of her plan to take the children and leave Serafin, even though such a thing was *infamante*. But then Serafin started to talk about America, and his old self came back, so she stayed with him and never mentioned the secret that she carried in her heart.

Serafin glanced over at Osvaldo, at his bare feet, the wet clothes. "What the devil were you doing in that river?" he

infamante Italian for "scandalous" or "shameful"

said. His voice was weak, but the words made sense now. Osvaldo stepped closer to his mother, keeping his eyes alert.

"It's okay," Lazzaro told him. "*Grazie a Dio*, nobody got hurt."

"Hurt?" Serafin shook his head, as if he did not understand the meaning of the word.

"Go get your shoes," Amalia scolded Osvaldo, the fear trembling beneath her words. Osvaldo trudged away, searching the riverbank for his shoes.

Serafin's own shoes were on his feet. He thought of this now, how if he had taken them off first it might have been easier to swim. He could have drowned because of a pair of shoes.

Step Hall was standing before him. He grasped Serafin's hand with a powerful grip and pulled him to his feet. Step squinted into Serafin's eyes, as if straining to see something. Serafin smiled uneasily, tried to move his hand away. But Step Hall squeezed the hand tighter in his. Serafin flinched from the pain.

"*Niente*, it's nothing," he told Step. "I did nothing." He looked around helplessly. "You—you saved us both."

Lazzaro laid a hand on Step's shoulder. Finally the man let go of Serafin. They stood awkwardly, like drunken men, unable to speak, not even knowing what it was they wanted to say.

Grazie a Dio Italian for "thank God"

Step looked out at the river, then over at his wife and boy a long time. His feet were lead. For all his dreams, he was useless after all. He turned and called gruffly for the group to move along. He lifted his son and laid him against his shoulder like a baby, and when he started walking his family and friends followed.

The Italians fell in behind them, Osvaldo barefoot and carrying his shoes in his hands while his father stumbled forward, steering the boy with one hand laid across his neck. Serafin squinted ahead at the dark shape resting in his father's arms: the boy who was not Valerio. Behind them Amalia and the girls trailed, subdued and silent, and Lazzaro and his wife and the old lady, back to the hay field below the levee, back to the sweet grass and the grazing cows and the acres of flat, silent, dusty land, away from the beautiful, merciless river. ❖

The White Umbrella

by Gish Jen

When I was twelve, my mother went to work without telling me or my little sister.

"Not that we need the second income." The **lilt** of her accent drifted from the kitchen up to the top of the stairs, where Mona and I were listening.

"No," said my father, in a barely **audible** voice. "Not like the Lee family."

The Lees were the only other Chinese family in town. I remembered how sorry my parents had felt for Mrs. Lee

....

lilt a lively, musical flow
audible able to be heard

when she started waitressing downtown the year before; and so when my mother began coming home late, I didn't say anything, and tried to keep Mona from saying anything either.

"But why shouldn't I?" she argued. "Lots of people's mothers work."

"Those are American people," I said.

"So what do you think we are? I can do the Pledge of Allegiance with my eyes closed."

Nevertheless, she tried to be **discreet**; and if my mother wasn't home by 5:30, we would start cooking by ourselves, to make sure dinner would be on time. Mona would wash the vegetables and put on the rice; I would chop.

For weeks we wondered what kind of work she was doing. I imagined that she was selling perfume, testing dessert recipes for the local newspaper. Or maybe she was working for the florist. Now that she had learned to drive, she might be delivering boxes of roses to people.

"I don't think so," said Mona as we walked to our piano lesson after school. "She would've hit something by now."

A gust of wind littered the street with leaves.

"Maybe we better hurry up," she went on, looking at the sky. "It's going to pour."

"But we're too early." Her lesson didn't begin until 4:00, mine until 4:30, so we usually tried to walk as slowly as we

....

discreet quiet; not attracting attention

could. "And anyway, those aren't the kind of clouds that rain. Those are **cumulus clouds**."

We arrived out of breath and wet.

"Oh, you poor, poor dears," said old Miss Crosman. "Why don't you call me the next time it's like this out? If your mother won't drive you, I can come pick you up."

"No, that's okay," I answered. Mona wrung her hair out on Miss Crosman's rug. "We just couldn't get the roof of our car to close, is all. We took it to the beach last summer and got sand in the **mechanism**." I pronounced this last word carefully, as if the **credibility** of my lie depended on its middle syllable. "It's never been the same." I thought for a second. "It's a convertible."

"Well then make yourselves at home." She exchanged looks with Eugenie Roberts, whose lesson we were interrupting. Eugenie smiled good-naturedly. "The towels are in the closet across from the bathroom."

Huddling at the end of Miss Crosman's nine-foot **leatherette** couch, Mona and I watched Eugenie play. She was a grade ahead of me and, according to school rumor, had a boyfriend in high school. I believed it. She had auburn hair, blue eyes, and, I noted with a particular **pang**, a pure white, folding umbrella.

....

cumulus clouds large, puffy, usually white clouds
mechanism moving part of a machine
credibility believability
leatherette fake leather
pang a sudden feeling of emotional pain or distress

"I can't see," whispered Mona.

"So clean your glasses."

"My glasses are clean. You're in the way."

I looked at her. "They look dirty to me."

"That's because your glasses are dirty."

Eugenie came bouncing to the end of her piece.

"Oh! Just **stupendous**!" Miss Crosman hugged her, then looked up as Eugenie's mother walked in. "Stupendous!" she said again. "Oh! Mrs. Roberts! Your daughter has a gift, a real gift. It's an honor to teach her."

Mrs. Roberts, **radiant** with pride, swept her daughter out of the room as if she were **royalty**, born to the piano bench. Watching the way Eugenie carried herself, I sat up, and concentrated so hard on sucking in my stomach that I did not realize until the Robertses were gone that Eugenie had left her umbrella. As Mona began to play, I jumped up and ran to the window, meaning to call to them—only to see their brake lights flash then fade at the stop sign at the corner. As if to allow them passage, the rain had let up; a quivering sun lit their way.

The umbrella glowed like a **scepter** on the blue carpet while Mona, slumping over the keyboard, managed to

....

stupendous superb; excellent; wonderful
radiant glowing
royalty belonging to a family of kings and queens
scepter a rod that a king or queen carries

eke out a fair **rendition** of a catfight. At the end of the piece, Miss Crosman asked her to stand up.

"Stay right there," she said, then came back a minute later with a towel to cover the bench. "You must be cold," she continued. "Shall I call your mother and have her bring over some dry clothes?"

"No," answered Mona. "She won't come because she …"

"She's too busy," I broke in from the back of the room.

"I see." Miss Crosman sighed and shook her head a little. "Your glasses are filthy, honey," she said to Mona. "Shall I clean them for you?"

Sisterly embarrassment seized me. Why hadn't Mona wiped her lenses when I told her to? As she resumed abuse of the piano, I stared at the umbrella. I wanted to open it, twirl it around by its slender silver handle; I wanted to dangle it from my wrist on the way to school the way the other girls did. I wondered what Miss Crosman would say if I offered to bring it to Eugenie at school tomorrow. She would be impressed with my consideration for others; Eugenie would be pleased to have it back; and I would have possession of the umbrella for an entire night. I looked at it again, toying with the idea of asking for one for Christmas. I knew, however, how my mother would react.

"Things," she would say. "What's the matter with a raincoat? All you want is things, just like an American."

eke out to do with great difficulty
rendition a performance

Sitting down for my lesson, I was careful to keep the towel under me and sit up straight.

"I'll bet you can't see a thing either," said Miss Crosman, reaching for my glasses. "And you can relax, you poor dear. This isn't a **boot camp**."

When Miss Crosman finally allowed me to start playing I played extra well, as well as I possibly could. See, I told her with my fingers. You don't have to feel sorry for me.

"That was wonderful," said Miss Crosman. "Oh! Just wonderful."

An entire constellation rose in my heart.

"And guess what," I announced proudly. "I have a surprise for you."

Then I played a second piece for her, a much more difficult one that she had not assigned.

"Oh! That was stupendous," she said without hugging me. "Stupendous! You are a genius, young lady. If your mother had started you younger, you'd be playing like Eugenie Roberts by now!"

I looked at the keyboard, wishing that I had still a third, even more difficult piece to play for her. I wanted to tell her that I was the school spelling bee champion, that I wasn't ticklish, that I could do karate.

"My mother is a concert pianist," I said.

----

boot camp a military camp in which new soldiers undergo very hard training

She looked at me for a long moment, then finally, without saying anything, hugged me. I didn't say anything about bringing the umbrella to Eugenie at school.

The steps were dry when Mona and I sat down to wait for my mother.

"Do you want to wait inside?" Miss Crosman looked anxiously at the sky.

"No," I said. "Our mother will be here any minute."

"In a while," said Mona.

"Any minute," I said again, even though my mother had been at least twenty minutes late every week since she started working.

According to the church clock across the street we had been waiting twenty-five minutes when Miss Crosman came out again.

"Shall I give you ladies a ride home?"

"No," I said. "Our mother is coming any minute."

"Shall I at least give her a call and remind her you're here? Maybe she forgot about you."

"I don't think she forgot," said Mona.

"Shall I give her a call anyway? Just to be safe?"

"I bet she already left," I said. "How could she forget about us?"

Miss Crosman went in to call.

"There's no answer," she said, coming back out.

"See, she's on her way," I said.

"Are you sure you wouldn't like to come in?"

"No," said Mona.

"Yes," I said. I pointed at my sister. "She meant yes, too. She meant no, she wouldn't like to go in."

Miss Crosman looked at her watch. "It's 5:30 now, ladies. My pot roast will be coming out in fifteen minutes. Maybe you'd like to come in and have some then?"

"My mother's almost here," I said. "She's on her way."

We watched and watched the street. I tried to imagine what my mother was doing; I tried to imagine her writing messages in the sky, even though I knew she was afraid of planes. I watched as the branches of Miss Crosman's big willow tree started to sway; they had all been trimmed to exactly the same height off the ground, so that they looked beautiful, like hair in the wind.

It started to rain.

"Miss Crosman is coming out again," said Mona.

"Don't let her talk you into going inside," I whispered.

"Why not?"

"Because that would mean Mom isn't really coming any minute."

"But she isn't," said Mona. "She's working."

"Shhh! Miss Crosman is going to hear you."

"She's working! She's working! She's working!"

I put my hand over her mouth, but she licked it, and so I was wiping my hand on my wet dress when the front door opened.

"We're getting even wetter," said Mona right away. "Wetter and wetter."

"Shall we all go in?" Miss Crosman pulled Mona to her feet. "Before you young ladies catch pneumonia? You've been out here an hour already."

"We're freezing." Mona looked up at Miss Crosman. "Do you have any hot chocolate? We're going to catch pneumonia."

"I'm not going in," I said. "My mother's coming any minute."

"Come on," said Mona. "Use your **noggin**."

"Any minute."

"Come on, Mona," Miss Crosman opened the door. "Shall we get you inside first?"

"See you in the hospital," said Mona as she went in. "See you in the hospital with pneumonia."

I stared out into the empty street. The rain was pricking me all over; I was cold; I wanted to go inside. I wanted to be able to let myself go inside. If Miss Crosman came out again, I decided, I would go in.

She came out with a blanket and the white umbrella.

I could not believe that I was actually holding the umbrella, opening it. It sprang up by itself as if it were alive, as if that were what it wanted to do—as if it belonged in my hands, above my head. I stared up at the network of silver spokes, then spun the umbrella around and around

noggin head

and around. It was so clean and white that it seemed to glow, to **illuminate** everything around it.

"It's beautiful," I said.

Miss Crosman sat down next to me, on one end of the blanket. I moved the umbrella over so that it covered that too. I could feel the rain on my left shoulder and shivered. She put her arm around me.

"You poor, poor dear."

I knew that I was in store for another bolt of sympathy, and braced myself by staring up into the umbrella.

"You know, I very much wanted to have children when I was younger," she continued.

"You did?"

She stared at me a minute. Her face looked dry and crusty, like day-old frosting.

"I did. But then I never got married."

I twirled the umbrella around again.

"This is the most beautiful umbrella I have ever seen," I said. "Ever, in my whole life."

"Do you have an umbrella?"

"No. But my mother's going to get me one just like this for Christmas."

"Is she? I tell you what. You don't have to wait until Christmas. You can have this one."

"But this one belongs to Eugenie Roberts," I protested. "I have to give it back to her tomorrow in school."

....

illuminate to light up

"Who told you it belongs to Eugenie? It's not Eugenie's. It's mine. And now I'm giving it to you, so it's yours."

"It is?"

She hugged me tighter. "That's right. It's all yours."

"It's mine?" I didn't know what to say. "Mine?" Suddenly I was jumping up and down in the rain. "It's beautiful! Oh! It's beautiful!" I laughed.

Miss Crosman laughed, too, even though she was getting all wet.

"Thank you, Miss Crosman. Thank you very much. Thanks a zillion. It's beautiful. It's stupendous!"

"You're quite welcome," she said.

"Thank you," I said again, but that didn't seem like enough. Suddenly I knew just what she wanted to hear. "I wish you were my mother."

Right away I felt bad.

"You shouldn't say that," she said, but her face was opening into a huge smile as the lights of my mother's car cautiously turned the corner. I quickly collapsed the umbrella and put it up my skirt, holding onto it from the outside, through the material.

"Mona!" I shouted into the house. "Mona! Hurry up! Mom's here! I told you she was coming!"

Then I ran away from Miss Crosman, down to the curb. Mona came tearing up to my side as my mother neared the house. We both backed up a few feet, so that in case she went onto the curb, she wouldn't run us over.

"But why didn't you go inside with Mona!" my mother asked on the way home. She had taken off her own coat to put over me, and had the heat on high.

"She wasn't using her noggin," said Mona, next to me in the back seat.

"I should call next time," said my mother. "I just don't like to say where I am."

That was when she finally told us that she was working as a check-out clerk in the **A&P**. She was supposed to be on the day shift, but the other employees were unreliable, and her boss had promised her a **promotion** if she would stay until the evening shift filled in.

For a moment no one said anything. Even Mona seemed to find the **revelation** disappointing.

"A promotion already!" she said, finally.

I listened to the windshield wipers.

"You're so quiet." My mother looked at me in the rear-view mirror. "What's the matter?"

"I wish you would quit," I said after a moment.

She sighed. "The Chinese have a saying: one beam cannot hold the roof up."

"But Eugenie Roberts's father supports their family."

She signed once more. "Eugenie Roberts's father is Eugenie Roberts's father," she said.

....

A&P at one time, a common grocery store chain
promotion advancement to a better job or higher position in a company
revelation something revealed or made known, usually something surprising

As we entered the downtown area, Mona started leaning hard against me every time the car turned right, trying to push me over. Remembering what I had said to Miss Crosman, I tried to **maneuver** the umbrella under my leg so she wouldn't feel it.

"What's under your skirt?" Mona wanted to know as we came to a traffic light. My mother, watching us in the rear-view mirror again, rolled slowly to a stop.

"What's the matter?" she asked.

"There's something under her skirt?" said Mona, pulling at me. "Under her skirt?"

Meanwhile, a man crossing the street started to yell at us. "Who do you think you are, lady?" he said. "You're blocking the whole crosswalk."

We all froze. Other people walking by stopped to watch.

"Didn't you hear me?" he went on, starting to thump on the hood with his fist. "Don't you speak English?"

My mother began to back up, but the car behind us honked. Luckily, the light turned green right after that. She sighed in relief.

"What were you saying, Mona?" she asked.

We wouldn't have hit the car behind us that hard if he hadn't been moving, too, but as it was our car bucked violently, throwing us all first back and then forward.

"Uh oh," said Mona when we stopped. "Another accident."

....

maneuver to move into a certain position

I was relieved to have attention **diverted** from the umbrella. Then I noticed my mother's head, tilted back onto the seat. Her eyes were closed.

"Mom!" I screamed. "Mom! Wake up!"

She opened her eyes. "Please don't yell," she said. "Enough people are going to yell already."

"I thought you were dead," I said, starting to cry. "I thought you were dead."

She turned around, looked at me intently, then put her hand to my forehead.

"Sick," she confirmed. "Some kind of sick is giving you crazy ideas."

As the man from the car behind us started tapping on the window, I moved the umbrella away from my leg. Then Mona and my mother were getting out of the car. I got out after them; and while everyone else was inspecting the damage we'd done, I threw the umbrella down a sewer. ❖

---

diverted turned aside

The Courage That My Mother Had

by Edna St. Vincent Millay

The courage that my mother had
Went with her, and is with her still:
Rock from New England **quarried**;
Now **granite** in a granite hill.

The golden **brooch** my mother wore
She left behind for me to wear;
I have no thing I treasure more:
Yet, it is something I could spare.

Oh, if instead she'd left to me
The thing she took into the grave!—
That courage like a rock, which she
Has no more need of, and I have. ❖

....

quarried removed from an open pit
granite a very hard rock
brooch a pin worn as jewelry, usually near the neck

Powerful Expression

Caring for Vets Should Be National Duty

by Christopher Dale

In advance of this year's Veterans Day, on Nov. 11, the **legions** of men and women who have served in our nation's military received some welcoming news: Congress finally agreed to fund the VA Mission Act, which since its June passage had been **mired** in budgetary disputes.

Announced on Sept. 11—an appropriate date—the arrangement sets aside more than $200 billion to improve the health care services provided by the U.S. Department of Veterans' Affairs.

Tales of delays and deficiencies, including long waits and poor access to proper care, have plagued the VA since injured vets started returning from Afghanistan and Iraq following 9/11. Last fall—16 years after the War on Terror began—the VA was still flooded with serious complaints about patient care; earlier this year, concerns about doctor shortages made headlines.

It's these issues that the VA Mission Act seeks to address. The law makes it easier for veterans to access covered care through non-VA service providers, who may be more

---

legions large numbers
mired swamped, stuck

convenient in terms of **expedience**, distance or quality
of care.

The law's primary principle is simple: Those injured
while serving in the military should not need to jump
through hoops for quality medical care.

The law also provides incentives for recruiting new doctors
to the VA, including an attractive education debt-relief
initiative and specialized training in afflictions4 most likely
to impact veterans, such as PTSD and painkiller addiction.

It's a terrific start, but the law has shortcomings.
For starters, despite settling the summer-long financial
squabble, Congress failed to deliver a long-term funding

expedience speed
afflictions medical conditions

solution for the law's historically high (though completely necessary) revenue requirements.

But the law's greatest disappointment is its narrowly defined view of caring for our injured veterans.

Tens of thousands of men and women have returned from Iraq and Afghanistan with permanent physical handicaps and deep emotional scars—wounds they will be coping with for the rest of their lives. Many need assistance outside the doctor's office, including finding suitable employment in an economy that, though humming for many, is far from ideal for individuals with disabilities, whose unemployment rate is more than double the national average.

Truly comprehensive care would not only fix the VA but expand it to empower injured veterans with economic opportunities, peer-to-peer engagement, and group-centric mental health programs that utilize injured veterans' greatest tool for overcoming battle-born trauma: each other.

Of course, nonprofit organizations like the Wounded Warrior Project have been offering these life-affirming tools for well over a decade. But why should it be up to private charities to take care of those who battled and bled for their country?

In a political landscape where we can't seem to agree on anything, it's likely that anyone—Democrat or Republication—would be challenged to find a single service provided by charities like the Wounded Warrior Project that doesn't deserve the full financial backing of the U.S. government.

We shouldn't have to pull on the heartstrings, and purse strings, of strangers to care for wounded war veterans in the United States. Their care should be provided, in full, by the American people.

The VA Mission Act is a step in the right direction, but we can—and should—go further by expanding the definition of what caring for injured veterans means. Our wounded veterans deserve not only exemplary health care, but all the tools they need to re-assimilate into civilian life despite missing limbs or shattered psyches. And to provide them what they are so obviously owed, the wealthiest country in the world should be relying on funding, not fundraising. ❖

Christopher Dale of Little Falls, New Jersey, writes on society, politics and sobriety-based issues. This column was written for the Progressive Media Project, which is run by The Progressive *magazine, and distributed by Tribune News Service.*

Nothing Gold Can Stay

by Robert Frost

Nature's first green is gold,
Her hardest **hue** to hold.
Her early leaf's a flower;
But only so an hour.
Then leaf **subsides** to leaf.
So **Eden** sank to grief,
So dawn goes down to day.
Nothing gold can stay. ❖

hue color; certain shade of a color
subsides falls; settles downward
Eden the biblical Garden of Eden; paradise

The Dragonfly

by Louise Bogan

You are made of almost nothing
But of enough
To be great eyes
And **diaphanous** double vans;
To be ceaseless movement,
Unending hunger,
Grappling love.

....

diaphanous extremely delicate and light; see-through
grappling struggling; wrestling

Link between water and air,
Earth repels you.
Light touches you only to shift into **iridescence**
Upon your body and wings.

Twice-born, predator,
You split into the heat.
Swift beyond calculation or capture
You dart into the shadow
Which consumes you.

You rocket into the day.
But at last, when the wind flattens the grasses,
For you, the design and purpose stop.

And you fall
With the other husks of summer. ❖

---

iridescence a spectrum of colors caused by refracted light waves

In Spite of War

by Angela Morgan

In spite of war, in spite of death,
In spite of all man's sufferings,
Something within me laughs and sings
And I must praise with all my breath.
In spite of war, in spite of hate
Lilacs are blooming at my gate,
Tulips are tripping down the path
In spite of war, in spite of wrath.
"Courage!" the morning-glory saith;
"Rejoice!" the daisy murmureth,
And just to live is so divine
When pansies lift their eyes to mine.

The clouds are **romping** with the sea,
And flashing waves call back to me
That **naught** is real but what is fair,
That everywhere and everywhere
A glory liveth through despair.
Though guns may roar and cannon boom,
Roses are born and gardens bloom;
My spirit still may light its flame
At that same torch **whence** poppies came.
Where morning's altar whitely burns
Lilies may lift their silver urns
In spite of war, in spite of shame.

And in my ear a whispering breath,
"Wake from the nightmare! Look and see
That life is naught but ecstasy
In spite of war, in spite of death!" ❖

---

romping playing or frolicking energetically
naught nothing
whence from where

The New Colossus

by Emma Lazarus

Not like the **brazen** giant of Greek fame,
With conquering limbs astride from land to land;
Here at our sea-washed, sunset gates shall stand
A mighty woman with a torch, whose flame
Is the imprisoned lightning, and her name
Mother of Exiles. From her beacon-hand
Glows world-wide welcome; her mild eyes command
The air-bridged harbor that twin cities frame.
"Keep, ancient lands, your storied **pomp**!" cries she
With silent lips. "Give me your tired, your poor,
Your huddled masses yearning to breathe free,
The wretched **refuse** of your **teeming** shore.
Send these, the homeless, **tempest**-tost to me,
I lift my lamp beside the golden door!" ❖

brazen bold; also, literally made of brass
pomp showy displays meant to be impressive
refuse things to be discarded; things considered to have no value
teeming full
tempest a violent storm

The Wind Begun to Rock the Grass

by Emily Dickinson

The Wind begun to rock the Grass
With threatening Tunes and low –
He threw a **Menace** at the Earth –
A Menace at the Sky.

The Leaves unhooked themselves from Trees –
And started all abroad
The Dust did scoop itself like Hands
And threw away the Road.

The Wagons quickened on the Streets
The Thunder hurried slow –
The Lightning showed a Yellow Beak
And then a **livid** Claw.

The Birds put up the Bars to Nests –
The Cattle fled to Barns –
There came one drop of Giant Rain
And then as if the Hands

That held the Dams had parted hold
The Waters Wrecked the Sky
But overlooked my Father's House –
Just **quartering** a Tree – ❖

....

menace a threat
livid very pale; very angry
quartering dividing into four pieces

I'll Tell You How the Sun Rose

by Emily Dickinson

I'll tell you how the Sun rose –
A Ribbon at a time –
The Steeples swam in **Amethyst** –
The news, like Squirrels, ran –

The Hills untied their Bonnets –
The **Bobolinks** – begun –
Then I said softly to myself –
"That must have been the Sun!"

But how he set – I know not –
There seemed a purple **stile**
That little Yellow boys and girls
Were climbing all the while –

Till when they reached the other side,
A **Dominie** in Gray –
Put gently up the evening Bars,
And led the flock away – ❖

....

amethyst a purple gem
bobolinks a kind of bird
stile steps that span across a wall or fence
Dominie a clergyman—for example, a priest

There Is No Frigate Like a Book

by Emily Dickinson

There is no **Frigate** like a Book
To take us Lands away
Nor any **Coursers** like a Page
Of prancing Poetry –
This **Traverse** may the poorest take
Without **oppress** of Toll –
How **frugal** is the Chariot
That bears the Human soul. ❖

frigate boat or ship
coursers fast horses
traverse a route; a way across
oppress a burden
frugal thrifty; inexpensive

Harlem [2]

by Langston Hughes

What happens to a dream **deferred**?

Does it dry up
like a raisin in the sun?
Or **fester** like a sore—
And then run?
Does it stink like rotten meat?
Or crust and sugar over—
like a syrupy sweet?

Maybe it just sags
like a heavy load.

Or does it explode? ❖

....

deferred put off; postponed
fester to make pus; to rot

241

Hold Fast Your Dreams

by Louise Driscoll

Hold fast your dreams!
Within your heart
Keep one still, secret spot
Where dreams may go,
And sheltered so,
May thrive and grow—
Where doubt and fear are not.
Oh, keep a place apart
Within your heart,
For little dreams to go. ❖

Truth and Identity

Homesick

by Jean Fritz

In my father's study there was a large globe with all the countries of the world running around it. I could put my finger on the exact spot where I was and had been ever since I'd been born. And I was on the wrong side of the globe. I was in China in a city named Hankow, a dot on a crooked line that seemed to break the country right in two. The line was really the **Yangtse River**, but who would know by looking at a map what the Yangtse River really was?

Orange-brown, muddy mustard-colored. And wide, wide, wide. With a river smell that was old and came all the way up from the bottom. Sometimes old women knelt on the riverbank, begging the River God to return a son or grandson who may have drowned. They would wail and beat the earth to make the River God pay attention, but I knew how busy the River God must be. All those people on the Yangtse River! **Coolies** hauling water. Women washing clothes. Houseboats swarming with old people and young, chickens and pigs. Big crooked-sailed **junks** with eyes painted on their **prows** so they could see where

Yangtse River (more commonly spelled *Yangtze*, and also called *Chang Jiang*) a very long river (more than 3,400 miles) flowing across central China and into the East China Sea

coolies unskilled laborers who do low-paying jobs

junks large, flat-bottomed ships with four-sided sails

prows fronts of ships

they were going. I loved the Yangtse River, but, of course,
I belonged on the other side of the world. In America with
my grandmother.

*Twenty-five fluffy little yellow chicks hatched from our eggs
today, my grandmother wrote.*

*I wrote my grandmother that I had watched a Chinese
magician swallow three yards of fire.*

The trouble with living on the wrong side of the world
was that I didn't feel like a real American.

For instance. I could never be president of the United
States. I didn't want to be president; I wanted to be a writer.
Still, why should there be a law saying that only a person

born in the United States could be president? It was as if I wouldn't be American enough.

Actually, I was American every minute of the day, especially during school hours. I went to a British school and every morning we sang "God Save the King." Of course the British children loved singing about their **gracious** king. Ian Forbes stuck out his chest and sang as if he were saving the king all by himself. Everyone sang. Even Gina Boss who was Italian. And Vera Sebastian who was so Russian she dressed the way Russian girls did long ago before the Revolution when her family had to run away to keep from being killed.

But I wasn't Vera Sebastian. I asked my mother to write an excuse so I wouldn't have to sing, but she wouldn't do it. "When in Rome," she said, "do as the Romans do." What she meant was, "Don't make trouble. Just sing." So for a long time I did. I sang with my fingers crossed but still I felt like a traitor.

Then one day I thought: If my mother and father were really truly in Rome, they wouldn't do what the Romans did at all. They'd probably try to get the Romans to do what *they* did, just as they were trying to teach the Chinese to do what Americans did. (My mother even gave classes in American manners.)

So that day I quit singing. I kept my mouth locked tight against the king of England. Our teacher, Miss Williams,

----

gracious kind; merciful

didn't notice at first. She stood in front of the room, using a ruler for a baton, striking each syllable so hard it was as if she were making up for the times she had nothing to strike.

(Miss Williams was pinch-faced and bossy. Sometimes I wondered what had ever made her come to China. "Maybe to try and catch a husband," my mother said.

A husband! Miss Williams!)

"Make him vic-tor-i-ous," the class sang. It was on the strike of "vic" that Miss Williams noticed. Her eyes lighted on my mouth and when we sat down, she pointed her ruler at me.

"Is there something wrong with your voice today, Jean?" she asked.

"No, Miss Williams."

"You weren't singing."

"No, Miss Williams. It is not my national anthem."

"It is the national anthem we sing here," she snapped. "You have always sung. Even Vera sings it."

I looked at Vera with the big blue bow tied on the top of her head. Usually I felt sorry for her but not today. At recess I might even untie that bow, I thought. Just give it a yank. But if I'd been smart, I wouldn't have been looking at Vera. I would have been looking at Ian Forbes and I would have known that, no matter what Miss Williams said, I wasn't through with the king of England.

Recess at the British School was nothing I looked forward to. Every day we played a game called prisoner's base, which was all running and shouting and shoving and catching. I hated the game, yet everyone played except Vera Sebastian. She sat on the **sidelines** under her blue bow like someone who had been dropped out of a history book. By recess I had forgotten my plans for that bow. While everyone was getting ready for the game, I was as usual trying to look as if I didn't care if I was the last one picked for a team or not. I was leaning against the high stone wall that ran around the schoolyard. I was looking up at a white cloud skittering across the sky when all at once someone tramped down hard on my right foot. Ian Forbes. Snarling bulldog face. Heel grinding down on my toes. Head thrust forward the way an animal might before it strikes.

"You wouldn't sing it. So say it," he ordered. "Let me hear you say it."

I tried to pull my foot away but he only ground down harder.

"Say what?" I was telling my face please not to show what my foot felt.

"*God save the king.* Say it. Those four words. I want to hear you say it."

Although Ian Forbes was short, he was solid and tough and built for fighting. What was more, he always won. You only had to look at his bare knees between the top of his socks and his short pants to know that he would win.

---

sidelines a place outside of or away from the action

His knees were square. Bony and unbeatable. So of course it was crazy for me to argue with him.

"Why should I?" I asked. "Americans haven't said that since George the Third."

He grabbed my right arm and twisted it behind my back.

"Say it," he hissed.

I felt the tears come to my eyes and I hated myself for the tears. I hated myself for not staying in Rome the way my mother had told me.

"I'll never say it," I whispered.

They were choosing sides now in the schoolyard and Ian's name was being called—among the first as always.

He gave my arm another twist. "You'll sing tomorrow," he snarled, "or you'll be bloody sorry."

As he ran off, I slid to the ground, my head between my knees.

Oh, Grandma, I thought, why can't I be there with you? I'd feed the chickens for you. I'd pump water from the well, the way my father used to do.

It would be almost two years before we'd go to America. I was ten years old now; I'd be twelve then. But how could I think about years? I didn't even dare to think about the next day. After school I ran all the way home, fast so I couldn't think at all.

Our house stood behind a high stone wall which had chips of broken glass sticking up from the top to keep thieves away. I flung open the iron gate and threw myself through the front door.

"I'm home!" I yelled.

Then I remembered it was Tuesday, the day my mother taught an English class at the **Y.M.C.A.** where my father was the director.

I stood in the hall, trying to catch my breath, and as always I began to feel small. It was a huge hall with ceilings so high it was as if they would have nothing to do with people. Certainly not with a mere child, not with me— the only child in the house. Once I asked my best friend, Andrea, if the hall made her feel little too. She said no. She was going to be a dancer and she loved space. She did a high kick to show how grand it was to have room.

Andrea Hull was a year older than I was and knew about everything sooner. She told me about commas, for instance, long before I took punctuation seriously. How could I write letters without commas? she asked. She made me so ashamed that for months I hung little wagging comma-tails all over the letters to my grandmother. She told me things that sounded so crazy I had to ask my mother if they were true. Like where babies come from. And that some day the whole world would end. My mother would frown when I asked her, but she always agreed that Andrea was right. It made me furious. How could she know

---

Y.M.C.A. Young Men's Christian Association

such things and not tell me? What was the matter with grown-ups anyway?

I wished Andrea were with me now, but she lived out in the country and I didn't see her often. Lin Nai-Nai, my **amah**, was the only one around, and of course I knew she'd be there. It was her job to stay with me when my parents were out. As soon as she heard me come in, she'd called, "Tsai loushang," which meant that she was upstairs. She might be mending or ironing but most likely she'd be sitting by the window embroidering. And she was. She even had my embroidery laid out, for we had made a bargain. She would teach me to embroider if I would teach her English. I liked embroidering: the cloth stretched tight within my embroidery hoop while I filled in the stamped pattern with cross-stitches and lazy daisy flowers. The trouble was that lazy daisies needed French knots for their centers and I hated making French knots. Mine always fell apart, so I left them to the end. Today I had twenty lazy daisies waiting for their knots.

Lin Nai-Nai had already threaded my needle with embroidery floss.

"Black centers," she said, "for the yellow flowers."

I felt myself **glowering**. "American flowers don't have centers," I said and gave her back the needle.

....

amah a nurse or nanny
glowering staring in an angry way; scowling

Lin Nai-Nai looked at me, puzzled, but she did not argue. She was different from other amahs. She did not even come from the servant class, although this was a secret we had to keep from the other servants who would have made her life miserable, had they known. She had run away from her husband when he had taken a second wife. She would always have been Wife Number One and the Boss no matter how many wives he had, but she would rather be no wife than head of a string of wives. She was modern. She might look old-fashioned, for her feet had been bound up tight when she was a little girl so they would stay small, and now, like many Chinese women, she walked around on little stumps stuffed into tiny cloth shoes. Lin Nai-Nai's were embroidered with butterflies. Still, she believed in true love and one wife for one husband. We were good friends, Lin Nai-Nai and I, so I didn't know why I felt so mean.

She shrugged. "English lesson?" she asked, smiling.

I tested my arm to see if it still hurt from the twist. It did. My foot too. "What do you want to know?" I asked.

We had been through polite phrases—Please, Thank you, I beg your pardon, Excuse me, You're welcome, Merry Christmas (which she had practiced but hadn't had a chance to use since this was only October).

"If I meet an American on the street," she asked, "how do I greet him?"

I looked her straight in the eye and nodded my head in greeting. "Sewing machine," I said. "You say 'Sew-ing ma-chine.'"

She repeated after me, making the four syllables into four separate words. She got up and walked across the room, bowing and smiling. "Sew Ing Ma Shing."

Part of me wanted to laugh at the thought of Lin Nai-Nai maybe meeting Dr. Carhart, our minister, whose face would surely puff up, the way it always did when he was **flustered**. But part of me didn't want to laugh at all. I didn't like it when my feelings got tangled, so I ran downstairs and played chopsticks on the piano. Loud and fast. When my sore arm hurt, I just beat on the keys harder.

Then I went out to the kitchen to see if Yang Sze-Fu, the cook, would give me something to eat. I found him reading a Chinese newspaper, his eyes going up and down with the characters. (Chinese words don't march across flat surfaces the way ours do; they drop down cliffs, one cliff after another from right to left across a page.)

"Can I have a piece of cinnamon toast?" I asked. "And a cup of cocoa?"

Yang Sze-Fu grunted. He was smoking a cigarette, which he wasn't supposed to do in the kitchen, but Yang Sze-Fu did mostly what he wanted. He considered himself superior to common workers. You could tell because of the fingernails on his pinkies. They were at least two inches

flustered upset due to being confused

long, which was his way of showing that he didn't have to use his hands for rough or dirty work. He didn't seem to care that his fingernails were dirty, but maybe he couldn't keep such long nails clean.

He made my toast while his cigarette dangled out of the corner of his mouth, collecting a long ash that finally fell on the floor. He wouldn't have kept smoking if my mother had been there, although he didn't always pay attention to my mother. Never about butter **pagodas**, for instance. No matter how many times my mother told him before a dinner party, "No butter pagoda," it made no difference. As soon as everyone was seated, the serving boy, Wong Sze-Fu, would bring in a pagoda and set it on the table. The guests would "oh" and "ah," for it was a masterpiece: a pagoda molded out of butter, curved roofs rising tier upon tier, but my mother could only think how unsanitary it was. For, of course, Yang Sze-Fu had molded the butter with his hands and carved the decorations with one of his long fingernails. Still, we always used the butter, for if my mother sent it back to the kitchen, Yang Sze-Fu would **lose face** and quit.

When my toast and cocoa were ready, I took them upstairs to my room (the blue room) and while I ate, I began *Sara Crewe* again. Now there was a girl, I thought, who was worth crying over. I wasn't going to think about myself. Or Ian Forbes. Or the next day. I wasn't. I wasn't.

....

pagodas in Asia, tower-like temples
lose face to be disgraced or dishonored

And I didn't. Not all afternoon. Not all evening. Still, I must have decided what I was going to do because the next morning when I started for school and came to the corner where the man sold hot chestnuts, the corner where I always turned to go to school, I didn't turn. I walked straight ahead. I wasn't going to school that day.

I walked toward the Yangtse River. Past the store that sold paper pellets that opened up into flowers when you dropped them in a glass of water. Then up the block where the beggars sat. I never saw anyone give money to a beggar. You couldn't, my father explained, or you'd be mobbed by beggars. They'd follow you everyplace; they'd never leave you alone. I had learned not to look at them when I passed and yet I saw. The running sores, the twisted legs, the mangled faces. What I couldn't get over was that, like me, each one of those beggars had one life to live. It just happened that they had drawn rotten ones.

Oh, Grandma, I thought, we may be far apart but we're lucky, you and I. Do you even know how lucky? In America do you know?

This part of the city didn't actually belong to the Chinese, even though the beggars sat there, even though the upper-class Chinese lived there. A long time ago other countries had just walked into China and divided up part of Hankow (and other cities) into sections, or concessions, which they called their own and used their own rules for governing. We lived in the French concession on **Rue de Paris**. Then there was the British concession and the Japanese. The Russian and German concessions had been officially returned to China, but the people still called them concessions. The Americans didn't have one, although, like some of the other countries, they had gunboats on the river. In case, my father said. In case what? Just in case. That's all he'd say.

The concessions didn't look like the rest of China. The buildings were **solemn** and orderly with little plots of grass around them. Not like those in the Chinese part of the city: a jumble of rickety shops with people, vegetables, crates of quacking ducks, yard goods, bamboo baskets, and mangy dogs spilling onto a street so narrow it was hardly there.

The grandest street in Hankow was the Bund, which ran along beside the Yangtse River. When I came to it after passing the beggars, I looked to my left and saw the American flag flying over the American **consulate** building. I was proud of the flag and I thought maybe it was proud of me. It flapped in the breeze as if it were saying ha-ha to the king of England.

Then I looked to the right at the **Customs House**, which stood at the other end of the Bund. The clock on top of the tower said nine-thirty. How would I spend the day?

....

Rue de Paris French for "Street of Paris"
solemn serious; gloomy
consulate the home or office of a government's representative in a foreign city
Customs House the office in which government officials inspect imported and exported goods and collect taxes ("customs") on them

I crossed the street to the **promenade** part of the Bund. When people walked here, they weren't usually going anyplace; they were just out for the air. My mother would wear her broad-brimmed beaver hat when we came and my father would swing his cane in that **jaunty** way that showed how glad he was to be a man. I thought I would just sit on a bench for the morning. I would watch the Customs House clock, and when it was time, I would eat the lunch I had brought along in my schoolbag.

I was the only one sitting on a bench. People did not generally "take the air" on a Wednesday morning and besides, not everyone was allowed here. The British had put a sign on the Bund, NO DOGS, NO CHINESE. This

promenade a public space meant for walking
jaunty lively; upbeat

meant that I could never bring Lin Nai-Nai with me. My father couldn't even bring his best friend, Mr. T. K. Hu. Maybe the British wanted a place where they could pretend they weren't in China, I thought. Still, there were always Chinese coolies around. In order to load and unload boats in the river, coolies had to cross the Bund. All day they went back and forth, bent double under their loads, sweating and chanting in a tired singsong way that seemed to get them from one step to the next.

To pass the time, I decided to recite poetry. The one good thing about Miss Williams was that she made us learn poems by heart and I liked that. There was one particular poem I didn't want to forget. I looked at the Yangtse River and pretended that all the busy people in the boats were my audience.

"'Breathes there the man, with soul so dead,'" I cried, "'Who never to himself hath said, This is my own, my native land!'"

I was so carried away by my performance that I didn't notice the policeman until he was right in front of me. Like all policemen in the British concession, he was a bushy-bearded Indian with a red **turban** wrapped around his head.

He pointed to my schoolbag. "Little miss," he said, "why aren't you in school?"

....

turban a long scarf wound around one's head

He was tall and mysterious-looking, more like a character in my Arabian Nights book than a man you expected to talk to. I fumbled for an answer. "I'm going on an errand," I said finally. "I just sat down for a rest." I picked up my schoolbag and walked quickly away. When I looked around, he was back on his corner, directing traffic.

So now they were chasing children away too, I thought angrily. Well, I'd like to show them. Someday I'd like to walk a dog down the whole length of the Bund. A Great Dane. I'd have him on a leash—like this—(I put out my hand as if I were holding a leash right then) and he'd be so big and strong I'd have to strain to hold him back (I strained). Then of course sometimes he'd have to do his business and I'd stop (like this) right in the middle of the sidewalk and let him go to it. I was so busy with my Great Dane I was at the end of the Bund before I knew it. I let go of the leash, clapped my hands, and told my dog to go home. Then I left the Bund and the concessions and walked into the Chinese world.

My mother and father and I walked here before but not for many months. This part near the river was called the Mud Flats. Sometimes it was muddier than others, and when the river flooded, the flats disappeared underwater. Sometimes even the fishermen's huts were washed away, knocked right off their long-legged stilts and swept down the river. But today the river was fairly low and the mud had dried so that it was cracked and cakey. Most of the men who lived here were out fishing, some not far from the shore, poling their **sampans** through the shallow water. Only a few people were on the flats: a man cleaning a fish on a flat rock at the water's edge, a woman spreading clothes on the dirt to dry, a few small children. But behind the huts was something I had never seen before. Even before I came close, I guessed what it was. Even then, I was excited by the strangeness of it.

It was the beginnings of a boat. The skeleton of a large junk, its ribs lying bare, its backbone running straight and true down the bottom. The outline of the prow was already in place, turning up wide and snub-nosed, the way all junks did. I had never thought of boats starting from nothing, of taking on bones under their bodies. The eyes, I supposed, would be the last thing added. Then the junk would have life.

The builders were not there and I was behind the huts where no one could see me as I walked around and around, **marveling**. Then I climbed inside and as I did, I knew that something wonderful was happening to me. I was a-tingle, the way a magician must feel when he swallows fire, because suddenly I knew the boat was mine. No matter who really owned it, it was mine. Even if I never saw it again, it would be my junk sailing up and down the Yangtse River. My junk seeing the river sights with its

....

sampans small, flat-bottomed boats
marveling feeling wonder, surprise, and amazement

two eyes, seeing them for me whether I was there or not. Often I had tried to put the Yangtse River into a poem so I could keep it. Sometimes I had tried to draw it, but nothing I did ever came close. But now, now I had my junk and somehow that gave me the river too.

I thought I should put my mark on the boat. Perhaps on the side of the spine. Very small. A secret between the boat and me. I opened my schoolbag and took out my folding penknife that I used for sharpening pencils. Very carefully I carved the Chinese character that was our name. Gau. (In China my father was Mr. Gau, my mother was Mrs. Gau, and I was Little Miss Gau.) The builders would paint right over the character, I thought, and never notice. But I would know. Always and forever I would know.

For a long time I dreamed about the boat, imagining it finished, its sails up, its eyes wide. Someday, it might sail all the way down the Yangtse to Shanghai, so I told the boat what it would see along the way because I had been there and the boat hadn't. After a while I got hungry and I ate my egg sandwich. I was in the midst of peeling an orange when all at once I had company.

A small boy, not more than four years old, wandered around to the back of the huts, saw me, and stopped still. He was wearing a ragged blue cotton jacket with a red cloth, pincushion-like charm around his neck which was supposed to keep him from getting **smallpox**. Sticking up

smallpox a dangerous contagious disease that in past times killed thousands straight from the middle of his head was a small pigtail which I knew was to fool the gods and make them think he was a girl. (Gods didn't bother much with girls; it was the boys that were important in China.) The weather was still warm so he wore no pants, nothing below the waist. Most small boys went around like this so that when they had to go, they could just let loose and go. He walked slowly up to the boat, stared at me, and then nodded as if he'd already guessed what I was. "Foreign devil," he announced gravely.

I shook my heard. "No," I said in Chinese. "American friend." Through the ribs of the boat, I handed him a segment of orange. He ate it slowly, his eyes on the rest of the orange. Segment by segment, I gave it all to him. Then he wiped his hands down the front of his jacket.

"Foreign devil," he repeated.

"American friend," I corrected. Then I asked him about the boat. Who was building it? Where were the builders?

He pointed with his chin upriver. "Not here today. Back tomorrow."

I knew it would only be a question of time before the boy would run off to alert the people in the huts. "Foreign devil, foreign devil," he would cry. So I put my hand on the prow of the boat, wished it luck, and climbing out, I stared back toward the Bund. To my surprise the boy walked beside me.

When we came to the edge of the Bund, I squatted down so we would be on the same eye level.

"Good-bye," I said. "May the River God protect you."

For a moment the boy stared. When he spoke, it was as if he were trying out a new sound. "American friend," he said slowly.

When I looked back, he was still there, looking soberly toward the foreign world to which I had gone.

The time, according to the Customs House clock, was five after two, which meant I couldn't go home for two hours. School was dismissed at three-thirty and I was home by three-forty-five unless I had to stay in for talking in class. It took me about fifteen minutes to write "I will not talk in class" fifty times, and so I often came home at four o'clock. (I wrote up and down like the Chinese: fifty "I's," fifty "wills," and right through the sentence so I never had to think what I was writing. It wasn't as if I were making a promise.) Today I planned to arrive home at four, my "staying-in" time, in the hope that I wouldn't meet classmates on the way.

Meanwhile I wandered up and down the streets, in and out of stores. I weighed myself on the big scale in the Hankow **Dispensary** and found that I was as skinny as ever. I went to the Terminus Hotel and tried out the chairs in the lounge. At first I didn't mind wandering about like this. Half of my mind was still on the river with my junk, but as time went on, my junk began slipping away until I

....

dispensary a medical clinic

was alone with nothing but questions. Would my mother find out about today? How could I skip school tomorrow? And the next day and the next? Could I get sick? Was there a kind of long lie-abed sickness that didn't hurt?

I arrived home at four, just as I had planned, opened the door, and called out, "I'm home!" Cheery-like and normal. But I was scarcely in the house before Lin Nai-Nai ran to me from one side of the hall and my mother from the other.

"Are you all right? Are you all right?" Lin Nai-Nai felt my arms as if she expected them to be broken. My mother's face was white. "What happened?" she asked.

Then I looked through the open door into the living room and saw Miss Williams sitting there. She had beaten me home and asked about my absence, which of course had scared everyone. But now my mother could see that I was in one piece and for some reason this seemed to make her mad. She took me by the hand and led me into the living room. "Miss Williams said you weren't in school," she said. "Why was that?"

I hung my head, just the way cowards do in books.

My mother dropped my hand. "Jean will be in school tomorrow," she said firmly. She walked Miss Williams to the door. "Thank you for stopping by."

Miss Williams looked satisfied in her mean, pinched way. "Well," she said, "ta-ta." (She always said "ta-ta" instead of "good-bye." Chicken language, it sounded like.)

As soon as Miss Williams was gone and my mother was sitting down again, I burst into tears. Kneeling on the floor, I buried my head in her lap and poured out the whole miserable story. My mother could see that I really wasn't in one piece after all, so she listened quietly, stroking my hair as I talked, but gradually I could feel her stiffen. I knew she was remembering that she was a Mother.

"You better go up to your room," she said, "and think things over. We'll talk about it after supper."

I flung myself on my bed. What was there to think? Either I went to school and got beaten up. Or I quit. After supper I explained to my mother and father how simple it was. I could stay at home and my mother could teach me, the way Andrea's mother taught her. Maybe I could even go to Andrea's house and study with her.

My mother shook her head. Yes, it was simple, she agreed. I could go back to the British School, be sensible, and start singing about the king again.

I clutched the edge of the table. Couldn't she understand? I couldn't turn back now. It was too late.

So far my father had not said a word. He was leaning back, teetering on the two hind legs of his chair, the way he always did after a meal, the way that drove my mother crazy. But he was not the type of person to keep all four legs on a chair on the floor just because someone wanted him to. He wasn't a turning-back person so I hoped maybe he would understand. As I watched him, I saw a twinkle start in his eyes and suddenly he brought his chair down slam-bang flat on the floor. He got up and motioned for us to follow him into the living room. He sat down at the piano and began to pick out the tune for "God Save the King."

A big help, I thought. Was he going to make me practice? Then he began to sing:

> "My country 'tis of thee,
> Sweet land of liberty, ..."

Of course! It was the same tune. Why hadn't I thought of that? Who would know what I was singing as long as I moved my lips? I joined in now, loud and strong.

> "Of thee I sing."

My mother laughed in spite of herself. "If you sing that loud," she said, "you'll start a revolution."

"Tomorrow, I'll sing softly," I promised. "No one will know." But for now I really let freedom ring.

Then all at once I wanted to see Lin Nai-Nai. I ran out back, through the courtyard that separated the house from the servants' quarters, and upstairs to her room.

"It's me," I called through the door and when she opened up, I threw my arms around her. "Oh, Lin Nai-Nai, I love you," I said. "You haven't said it yet, have you?"

"Said what?"

"Sewing machine. You haven't said it?"

"No," she said, "not yet. I'm still practicing."

"Don't say it, Lin Nai-Nai. Say 'Good day.' It's shorter and easier. Besides, it's more polite."

"Good day?" she repeated.

"Yes, that's right. Good day." I hugged her and ran back to the house.

The next day at school when we rose to sing the British national anthem, everyone stared at me, but as soon as I opened my mouth, the class lost interest. All but Ian Forbes. His eyes never left my face, but I sang softly, carefully, proudly. At recess he **sauntered** over to where I stood against the wall.

He spat on the ground. "You can be bloody glad you sang today," he said. Then he strutted off as if he and those square knees of his had won again.

And, of course, I was bloody glad. ❖

....

sauntered walked casually

Mami and Papi

from When I Was Puerto Rican
by Esmeralda Santiago

We came to Macún when I was four, to a rectangle of
ripped metal sheets on stilts hovering in the middle of
a circle of red dirt. Our home was a giant version of the
lard cans used to haul water from the public fountain. Its
windows and doors were also metal, and, as we stepped in,
I touched the wall and burned my fingers.

"That'll teach you," Mami scolded. "Never touch a wall
on the sunny side."

She searched a bundle of clothes and diapers for her jar
of Vick's VapoRub to smear on my fingers. They were red the
rest of the day, and I couldn't suck my thumb that night.

"You're too big for that anyway," she said.

The floor was a patchwork of odd-shaped wooden
slats that rose in the middle and dipped toward the front
and back doors, where they butted against shiny, worn
thresholds. Papi nailed new boards under Mami's **treadle**
sewing machine, and under their bed, but the floor still
groaned and sagged to the corners, threatening to collapse
and bring the house down with it.

---

thresholds doorsills; planks or stones under a door
treadle the pedal that operates an old sewing machine

House similar to one the author might have lived in

"I'll rip the whole thing out," Papi suggested. "We'll have to live with a dirt floor for a while…"

Mami looked at her feet and shuddered. A dirt floor, we'd heard, meant snakes and scorpions could crawl into the house from their holes in the ground. Mami didn't know any better, and I had yet to learn not everything I heard was true, so we reacted in what was to become a pattern for us: what frightened her I became curious about, and what she found exciting terrified me. As Mami pulled her feet onto the rungs of her rocking chair and rubbed the goose bumps from her arms, I imagined a world of fascinating creatures slithering underfoot, drawing squiggly patterns on the dirt.

The day Papi tore up the floor, I followed him holding a can into which he dropped the straight nails, still usable. My fingers itched with a rust-colored powder, and when I licked them, a dry, metallic taste curled the tip of my tongue. Mami stood on the threshold scratching one ankle with the toes of the other foot.

"Negi, come help me gather **kindling** for the fire."

"I'm working with Papi," I whined, hoping he'd ask me to stay. He didn't turn around but continued on his knees, digging out nails with the hammer's claw, muttering the words to his favorite chachachá.

"Do as I say!" Mami ordered. Still, Papi kept his back to us. I plunked the can full of nails down hard, willing him to hear and tell me to stay, but he didn't. I **dawdled** after Mami down the three steps into the yard. Delsa and Norma, my younger sisters, took turns swinging from a rope Papi had hung under the mango tree.

"Why can't they help with the kindling?" I pouted. Mami swatted the side of my head. "Don't talk back," she said. "You girls keep away from the house while your father is working," she warned as we walked by my sisters having fun.

She led the way into a thicket behind the **latrine**. Twigs crackled under my bare feet, stinging the soles.

....

kindling material used to start a fire, such as dry sticks or leaves
dawdled moved slowly and aimlessly
latrine an outdoor, shared bathroom

A **bananaquit** flew to the thorny branch of a lemon tree and looked from side to side. Dots of sun danced on the green walls of the shady grove above low bushes weighted with pigeon peas, the earth screened with twigs, sensitive *morivivi* plants, and french weed studded with tiny blue flowers. Mami hummed softly, the yellow and orange flowers on her dress blending into the greenness: a **miraculous** garden with legs and arms and a melody. Her hair, choked at the **nape** with a rubber band, floated thick and black to her waist, and as she bent over to pick up sticks, it rained across her shoulders and down her arms, covering her face and tangling in the twigs she cradled. A red butterfly circled her and flew close to her ear. She gasped and swatted it into a bush.

"It felt like it was going right into my brain," she muttered with an embarrassed smile.

Delsa and Norma toddled through the underbrush. "Mami, come see what I found," Delsa called.

A hen had scratched out a hollow and carpeted its walls and floor with dry grass. She had laid four eggs, smaller and not as white as the ones our neighbor **Doña** Lola gave us from time to time.

....

bananaquit a small, colorful bird commonly found in warm climates
morivivi a flower common in Puerto Rico and other parts of the Caribbean
miraculous like a miracle; marvelous
nape the back of the neck
Doña in Spanish, a respectful title for a woman

"Can we eat them?" Delsa asked.

"No."

"But if we leave them here a snake will get them," I said, imagining a serpent swallowing each egg whole. Mami shuddered and rubbed her arms where tiny bumps had formed making the fine hairs stand straight up. She gave me a look, half puzzled, half angry, and drew us to her side.

"All right, let's get our sticks together and bring them to the kitchen." As she picked hers up, she looked carefully around.

"One, two, three, four," she chanted. "One, two, three, four." We marched single file into our yard, where Papi stacked floorboards.

"Come look," he said.

The dirt was orange, striped in places where crumbs had slipped through the cracks when Mami swept. Papi had left a few boards down the center of the room and around his and Mami's bed, to stand on until the ground was swept and flattened. Mami was afraid to come into the house. There were small holes in the dirt, holes where snakes and scorpions hid. She turned swiftly and threw herself off balance so that she skipped toward the kitchen shed.

"Let's go make supper!" She singsang to make it sound like fun. Delsa and Norma followed her skirt, but I stared at the dirt, where squiggly lines stretched from one wall to the other. Mami waited for me.

"Negi, come help in the kitchen."

I pretended not to hear but felt her eyes bore holes in the back of my head. Papi stepped between us.

"Let her stay. I can use the help."

I peered between his legs and saw her squint and pucker her lips as if she were about to spit. He chuckled, "Heh, heh," and she whirled toward the kitchen shed, where the fire in the *fogón* was almost out.

"Take these boards and lay them on the pile for the cooking fire," Papi said. "Careful with the splinters."

I walked a broad circle around Mami, who looked up from her vegetable chopping whenever I went by. When I passed carrying a wide board, Mami asked to see it. Black bugs, like ants, but bigger and blacker, crawled over it in a **frenzy**.

"Termites!" she gasped.

I was covered with them. They swarmed inside my shirt and panties, into my hair, under my arms. Until Mami saw them, I hadn't felt them sting. But they bit ridges into my skin that itched and hurt at the same time. Mami ran me to the washtub and dunked me among my father's soaking shirts.

"Pablo!" she called, "Oh, my God! Look at her. She's being eaten alive!"

---

fogón Spanish word meaning "fireplace" or "furnace"
frenzy a state of wild excitement

I screamed, imagining my skin disappearing in chunks into the invisible mouths of hundreds of tiny black specks creeping into parts of my body I couldn't even reach. Mami pulled off my clothes and threw them on the ground. The soap in the washtub burned my skin, and Mami scrubbed me so hard her fingernails dug angry **furrows** into my arms and legs. She turned me around to wash my back, and I almost fell out of the tub.

"Be still," she said. "I have to get them all."

She pushed and shoved and turned me so fast I didn't know what to do with my body, so I **flailed**, seeming to resist, while in fact I wanted nothing more than to be rid of the creepy crawling things that covered me. Mami wrapped me in a towel and lifted me out of the tub with a groan. Hundreds of black bugs floated between the bubbles.

She carried me to the house pressed against her bosom, fragrant of curdled milk. Delsa and Norma ran after us, but Papi scooped them up, one on each arm, and carried them to the rope swing. Mami balanced on the floorboards to her bed, lay me beside her, held me tight, kissed my forehead, my eyes, and murmured, "It's all right. It's over. It's all right."

I wrapped my legs around her and buried my face under her chin. It felt so good to have Mami so close, so

....

furrows grooves, like the tracks left by a plow
flailed moved as though beating or striking something

warm, **swathed** by her softness, her smell of wood smoke and **oregano**. She rubbed circles on my back and **caressed** the hair from my face. She kissed me, brushed my tears with her fingertips, and dried my nose with the towel, or the hem of her dress.

"You see," she murmured, "what happens when you don't do what I say?"

I turned away from her and curled into a tight ball of shame. Mami rolled off the bed and went outside. I lay on her pillow, whimpering, wondering how the termites knew I'd disobeyed my mother. ❖

....

swathed wrapped; covered
oregano an herb used as a seasoning
caressed gently stroked or rubbed

The Night the Bed Fell

by James Thurber

I suppose that the **high-water mark** of my youth in
Columbus, Ohio, was the night the bed fell on my father.
It makes a better **recitation** (unless, as some friends of
mine have said, one has heard it five or six times) than it
does a piece of writing, for it is almost necessary to throw
furniture around, shake doors, and bark like a dog,
to lend the proper atmosphere and **verisimilitude** to
what is admittedly a somewhat incredible tale. Still, it
did take place.

It happened, then, that my father had decided to sleep
in the attic one night, to be away where he could think.
My mother opposed the notion strongly because, she said,
the old wooden bed up there was unsafe: it was wobbly and
the heavy headboard would crash down on father's head
in case the bed fell, and kill him. There was no **dissuading**
him, however, and at a quarter past ten he closed the attic
door behind him and went up the narrow twisting stairs.
We later heard **ominous** creakings as he crawled into bed.
Grandfather, who usually slept in the attic bed when

----

high-water mark highest point; most notable moment or occurrence
recitation a spoken presentation
verisimilitude the appearance of being true
dissuading persuading not to do something; advising against
ominous threatening; signaling danger

he was with us, had disappeared some days before. (On these occasions he was usually gone six or seven days and returned growling and out of temper, with the news that the **Federal Union** was run by a **passel** of blockheads and that the **Army of the Potomac** didn't have a chance.)

We had visiting us at this time a nervous first cousin of mine named Briggs Beall, who believed that he was likely to cease breathing when he was asleep. It was his feeling that if he were not awakened every hour during the night, he might die of suffocation. He had been accustomed to setting an alarm clock to ring at intervals until morning, but I persuaded him to abandon this. He slept in my room and I told him that I was such a light sleeper that if anybody quit breathing in the same room with me, I would wake instantly. He tested me the first night—which I had suspected he would—by holding his breath after my regular breathing had convinced him I was asleep. I was not asleep, however, and called to him. This seemed to **allay** his fears a little, but he took the precaution of putting a glass of spirits of **camphor** on a little table at the head of his bed. In case I didn't arouse him until he was almost gone, he said, he would sniff the camphor, a powerful reviver.

....

Federal Union in the Civil War, the North
passel a large number of something
Army of the Potomac one of the Northern armies during the Civil War
allay to ease; to calm
camphor a substance with a strong odor, sometimes used for medical purposes

Briggs was not the only member of his family who had his **crotchets**. Old Aunt Melissa Beall (who could whistle like a man, with two fingers in her mouth) suffered under the **premonition** that she was destined to die on South High Street, because she had been born on South High Street and married on South High Street. Then there was Aunt Sarah Shoaf, who never went to bed at night without the fear that a burglar was going to get in and blow **chloroform** under her door through a tube. To avert this **calamity**—for she was in greater dread of **anesthetics** than of losing her household goods—she always piled her money, silverware, and other valuables in a neat stack just outside her bedroom, with a note reading: "This is all I have. Please take it and do not use your chloroform, as this is all I have." Aunt Gracie Shoaf also had a burglar phobia, but she met it with more **fortitude**. She was confident that burglars had been getting into her house every night for four years. The fact that she never missed anything was to her no proof to the contrary. She always claimed that she scared them off before they could take anything, by throwing shoes down the hallway. When she went to bed

crotchets odd habits
premonition a feeling that something (usually bad) is soon to happen
chloroform a substance that can render people unconscious, once frequently used as an anesthetic
calamity disaster; catastrophe
anesthetics substances used to take away feeling, sometimes by rendering a person unconscious
fortitude strength and determination in the face of challenges

she piled, where she could get at them handily, all the shoes there were about her house. Five minutes after she had turned off the light, she would sit up in bed and say "Hark!" Her husband, who had learned to ignore the whole situation as long ago as 1903, would either be sound asleep or pretend to be sound asleep. In either case he would not respond to her tugging and pulling, so that presently she would arise,

tiptoe to the door, open it slightly and heave a shoe down the hall in one direction, and its mate down the hall in the other direction. Some nights she threw them all, some nights only a couple of pair.

But I am straying from the remarkable incidents that took place during the night that the bed fell on father. By midnight we were all in bed. The layout of the rooms and the **disposition** of their occupants is important to an understanding of what later occurred. In the front room upstairs (just under father's attic bedroom) were my

disposition arrangement; placement

mother and my brother Terry, who sometimes sang in his sleep, usually "Marching Through Georgia" or "Onward, Christian Soldiers." Briggs Beall and myself were in a room adjoining this one. My brother Roy was in a room across the hall from ours. Our bull terrier, Rex, slept in the hall.

My bed was an army cot, one of those affairs which are made wide enough to sleep on comfortably only by putting up, flat with the middle section, the two sides which ordinarily hang down like the sideboards of a drop-leaf table. When these sides are up, it is **perilous** to roll too far toward the edge, for then the cot is likely to tip completely over, bringing the whole bed down on top of one, with a tremendous banging crash. This, in fact, is precisely what happened, about two o'clock in the morning. (It was my mother who, in recalling the scene later, first referred to it as "the night the bed fell on your father.")

Always a deep sleeper, slow to arouse (I had lied to Briggs), I was at first unconscious of what had happened when the iron cot rolled me onto the floor and toppled over on me. It left me still warmly bundled up and unhurt, for the bed rested above me like a canopy. Hence I did not wake up, only reached the edge of consciousness and went back. The racket, however, instantly awakened my mother, in the next room, who came to the immediate conclusion that her worst dread was realized: the big wooden bed

....

perilous dangerous

upstairs had fallen on father. She therefore screamed, "Let's go to your poor father!" It was this shout, rather than the noise of my cot falling, that awakened Herman, in the same room with her. He thought that mother had become, for no apparent reason, hysterical. "You're all right, Mamma!" he shouted, trying to calm her. They exchanged shout for shout for perhaps ten seconds: "Let's go to your poor father!" and "You're all right!" That woke up Briggs. By this time I was conscious of what was going on, in a vague way, but did not yet realize that I was under my bed instead of on it. Briggs, awakening in the midst of loud shouts of fear and apprehension, came to the quick conclusion that he was suffocating and that we were all trying to "bring him out." With a low moan, he grasped the glass of camphor at the head of his bed and instead of sniffing it poured it over himself. The room reeked of camphor. "Ugf, ahfg," choked Briggs, like a drowning man, for he had almost succeeded in stopping his breathing under the **deluge** of **pungent** spirits. He leaped out of bed and groped toward the open window, but he came up against one that was closed. With his hand, he beat out the glass, and I could hear it crash and tinkle on the alleyway below. It was at this **juncture** that I, in trying to get up,

....

deluge a flood
pungent having a sharp, stinging smell
juncture a point in time at which events come together in some significant way

had the **uncanny** sensation of feeling my bed above me! Foggy with sleep, I now suspected, in my turn, that the whole uproar was being made in a **frantic endeavor** to **extricate** me from what must be an unheard-of and perilous situation. "Get me out of this!" I bawled. "Get me out!" I think I had the nightmarish belief that I was entombed in a mine. "Gugh," gasped Briggs, **floundering** in his camphor.

By this time my mother, still shouting, pursued by Herman, still shouting, was trying to open the door to the attic, in order to go up and get my father's body out of the wreckage. The door was stuck, however, and wouldn't yield. Her frantic pulls on it only added to the general banging and confusion. Roy and the dog were now up, the one shouting questions, the other barking.

....

uncanny weird; eerie; mysterious
frantic wildly anxious; panicky
endeavor an effort; an attempt
extricate to free from a difficult position or situation
floundering moving clumsily

Father, farthest away and soundest sleeper of all, had by this time been awakened by the battering on the attic door. He decided that the house was on fire. "I'm coming, I'm coming!" he wailed in a slow, sleepy voice—it took him many minutes to regain full consciousness. My mother, still believing he was caught under the bed, detected in his "I'm coming!" the mournful, resigned note of one who is preparing to meet his Maker. "He's dying!" she shouted.

"I'm all right!" Briggs yelled to reassure her. "I'm all right!" He still believed that it was his own closeness to death that was worrying mother. I found at last the light switch in my room, unlocked the door, and Briggs and I joined the others at the attic door. The dog, who never did like Briggs, jumped for him—assuming that he was the **culprit** in whatever was going on—and Roy had to throw Rex and hold him. We could hear father crawling out of bed upstairs. Roy pulled the attic door open with a mighty jerk, and father came down the stairs, sleepy and irritable but safe and sound. My mother began to weep when she saw him. Rex began to howl. "What in the name of God is going on here?" asked father.

The situation was finally put together like a gigantic jig-saw puzzle. Father caught a cold from prowling around in his bare feet but there were no other bad results. "I'm glad," said mother, who always looked on the bright side of things, "that your grandfather wasn't here." ❖

culprit a guilty person

Eileen Collins—NASA's First Female Shuttle Commander to Lead Next Shuttle Mission

October 4, 2003

courtesy of NASAexplores

On her last mission, Eileen Collins became the first (and currently only) female Shuttle commander. On her next, she will command the historic STS-114 "Return to Flight" mission, the first after the *Columbia* tragedy.

On becoming an astronaut: "When I was very young and first started reading about astronauts, there were no women astronauts." However, she was inspired while she was a child by the Mercury astronauts, and by the time she was in high school and college, new opportunities were opening up for women in **aviation**. "My timing was really great," she said. Collins joined the Air Force, and during her first month of training, her base was visited by the newest astronaut class—the first to include women—and her path was set. "I wanted to be part of our nation's space program. It's the greatest adventure on this planet—or off the planet, for that matter. I wanted to fly the Space Shuttle."

On being the first and only female Shuttle commander: "Hopefully not for long!" While the **distinction** of being

aviation the flying of aircraft
distinction a difference that sets one apart from others

Eileen Collins (far right) with the other crew members of the Space Shuttle *Discovery*, July 13, 2005

the first is an honor, Collins said she's looking forward to losing the part about being the "only" female commander. She said she hopes current astronaut Pam Melroy will soon join her, and that more will follow. "I'm really pulling for her." Collins said that she encourages young women to become test pilots so that they can someday become Shuttle commanders as well. "The young people are going to be the ones to take us on to more exciting adventures."

On her advice for future astronauts: "My advice to young people is, go into the field you are most interested in. If you love your job, you'll do well in your job." While coming from a mathematics, science, or technology background is a must, there's a lot of variety in what exactly you can pursue. In fact, Collins discourages people from looking at what other astronauts are in and choosing that. The exact opposite worked for her—when she joined the corps, there were no astronauts in her field, operations research. "I said I think I can fill a **void**, and I think they bought it." It's paid off, too, she said, since much of her background ties in directly to the operation of the Shuttle.

On the most exciting thing about spaceflight: "If you had asked me this question after my first mission, I would would have said the launch. Now, I would say seeing the successful completion of the mission." As an example, she cited the first mission she commanded, STS-93, on which the Chandra X-Ray Observatory was deployed. There were

....

void an empty space

Biographical Data

Hometown: Elmira, New York

Born: November 19, 1956

Education: Associate degree in mathematics/science from Corning Community College; bachelor's degree in mathematics and economics from Syracuse University; master's degree in operations research from Stanford University; master's degree in space systems management from Webster University

so many people involved in the Chandra project and the launch, she said, and it's been really rewarding seeing the amazing pictures that Chandra has taken. "Everybody came together and made it happen."

On her upcoming first visit to the International Space Station (ISS): "It's hard to wait. I'm so excited." In fact, she said, the opportunity to visit the ISS is why she decided to keep flying at a point in her career when many astronauts retire from spaceflight. "I had never gone to the Station, and I really wanted to go to there. I really wanted to be part of the Station mission."

On the future of spaceflight: "I would like to see more people traveling to space someday. I would like to see space tourism blossom. It's such an incredible experience."

Spaceflight Experience:
- Pilot, *Discovery* STS-63—Collins became the first female Shuttle pilot during this 1995 mission, which included a rendezvous with the Russian Space Station *Mir*.
- Pilot, *Atlantis* STS-84—This 1997 mission transferred supplies to the *Mir* Space Station.
- Commander, *Columbia* STS-93—Collins became the first female Shuttle commander on this 1999 mission, which included the deployment of the Chandra X-Ray Observatory.

Collins said that during her spaceflights, there is so much she has to do that there is little time to just enjoy being in space. "Someday I would like to go into space as a tourist, and have the time to have fun." She's very interested in developments in the field of **civilian** spaceflight, such as the X Prize competition. "I just think that's really exciting. That's an experience that more people ought to have. I think we'd have a better community on Earth if more people traveled in space."

On her upcoming "Return to Flight" mission: "We're very excited. We're very confident." While they're waiting for their next flight, Collins said, her crew has been involved in research on making the Space Shuttle more safe, and has been visiting the factories involved in the Space Shuttle program and meeting the workers. "When the Shuttle's ready to fly, we'll be ready to fly." ❖

civilian relating to people who are not in the military, police force, or firefighting force

excerpt from

President Richard M. Nixon's News Conference: The President's Personal Finances

November 17, 1973
Annual Convention of the Associated Press
Managing Editors Association, Orlando, Florida

[To the next questioner] Let me just respond, if I could, sir, before going to your question—I will turn left and then come back to the right; I don't want to tilt either way at the moment, as you can be sure—since the question was raised a moment ago about my tax payments.

I noted in some editorials and perhaps in some commentaries on television, a very reasonable question. They said, you know, "How is it that President Nixon could have a very heavy investment in a fine piece of property in San Clemente and a big investment in a piece of property in Florida," in which I have two houses, one which I **primarily** use as an office and the other as a residence, and also an investment in what was my mother's home, not very much of a place but I do own it—those three pieces of property.

I want to say first, that is all I have. I am the first president since Harry Truman who hasn't owned any stock

....

primarily mainly

since ever I have been president. I am the first one who has not had a blind trust since Harry Truman. Now, that doesn't prove that those who owned stocks or had blind trusts did anything wrong. But I felt that in the presidency it was important to have no question about the president's personal finances, and I thought real estate was the best place to put it.

But then, the question was raised by good editorial writers—and I want to respond to it because some of you might be too polite to ask such an embarrassing question—they said, "Now, Mr. President, you earned $800,000 when you were president. Obviously, you paid at least half that much or could have paid half that much in taxes or a great deal of it—how could you possibly have had the money? Where did you get it?"

And then, of course, overriding all of that is the story to the effect that I have a million dollars in campaign funds, which was broadly printed throughout this country with **retractions** not quite getting quite as much play as the printing of the first, and particularly not on television. The newspapers did much better than television in that respect, I should point out.

And second, they said, "How is it that as far as this money is concerned, how is it possible for you to have this kind of investment when all you earned was $800,000 as president?"

....

retractions withdrawals of previous statements or claims

Well, I should point out I wasn't a **pauper** when I became President. I wasn't very rich as presidents go. But you see, in the eight years that I was out of office—first, just to put it all out and I will give you a paper on this, we will send it around to you, and these figures I would like you to have, not today, but I will have it in a few days— when I left office after four years as a Congressman, [three] years as a Senator, and eight years at $45,000 a year as vice president, and after stories had been written, particularly in

President Richard M. Nixon addressing conference attendees, November 17, 1973

the *Washington Post* to the effect that the [vice] president had purchased a mansion in Wesley Heights and people wondered where the money came from, you know what my net worth was? Forty-seven thousand dollars total, after fourteen years of government service, and a 1958 Oldsmobile that needed an overhaul.

Now, I have no complaints. In the next eight years, I made a lot of money. I made $250,000 from a book and the serial rights which many of you were good enough

pauper an impoverished or extremely poor individual

to purchase, also. In the practice of law—and I am not claiming I was worth it, but apparently former vice presidents or presidents are worth a great deal to law firms—and I did work pretty hard.

But also in that period, I earned between $100,000 and $250,000 every year.

So that when I, in 1968, decided to become a candidate for president, I decided to clean the decks and to put everything in real estate. I sold all my stock for $300,000— that is all I owned. I sold my apartment in New York for $300,000—I am using rough figures here. And I had $100,000 coming to me from the law firm.

And so, that is where the money came from. Let me just say this, and I want to say this to the television audience: I made my mistakes, but in all of my years of public life, I have never profited, never profited from public service—I have earned every cent. And in all of my years of public life, I have never **obstructed** justice. And I think, too, that I could say that in my years of public life, that I welcome this kind of examination because people have got to know whether or not their President is a crook. Well, I am not a crook. I have earned everything I have got. ❖

---

obstructed blocked or deliberately prevented

President Richard M. Nixon: Re-Election, Second Term, and Watergate

courtesy of the Nixon Presidential Library and Museum

In his 1972 bid for re-election, Nixon defeated South Dakota Senator George McGovern, the Democratic candidate for president, by one of the widest electoral margins ever, winning 520 electoral college votes to McGovern's 17 and nearly 61 percent of the popular vote. Just a few months later, investigations and public controversy over the Watergate scandal had sapped Nixon's popularity. The Watergate scandal began with the June 1972 discovery of a break-in at the Democratic National Committee offices in the Watergate office complex in Washington, D.C., but media and official investigations soon revealed a broader pattern of abuse of power by the Nixon administration, leading to his resignation.

The Watergate burglars were soon linked to officials of the Committee to Re-Elect the President, the group that had run Nixon's 1972 re-election campaign. Soon thereafter, several administration officials resigned; some, including former attorney general John Mitchell, were later convicted of offenses connected with the break-in and other crimes and went to jail. Nixon denied any personal involvement with the Watergate burglary, but the courts forced him to yield tape recordings of conversations between the president and his advisers indicating that the president had, in fact, participated in the cover-up, including an attempt to use the Central Intelligence Agency to **divert** the FBI's investigation into the break-in.

Investigations into Watergate also revealed other abuses of power, including numerous warrantless wiretaps on reporters and others, campaign "dirty tricks," and the creation of a "Plumbers" unit within the White House. The Plumbers, formed in response to the leaking of the Pentagon Papers to news organizations by former Pentagon official Daniel Ellsberg, broke into the office of Ellsberg's psychiatrist.

Adding to Nixon's worries was an investigation into Vice President Agnew's ties to several campaign contributors. The Department of Justice found that Agnew had taken bribes from Maryland construction firms, leading to Agnew's resigning in October 1973 and his entering a plea of no contest to income tax evasion. Nixon nominated Gerald Ford, Republican leader in the House of Representatives, to succeed Agnew. Ford was confirmed by both houses of Congress and took office on December 6, 1973.

Such controversies all but overshadowed Nixon's other initiatives in his second term, such as the signing of the Paris peace accords ending American involvement in the Vietnam War in January 1973; two summit meetings with Brezhnev, in June 1973 in Washington and in June and July 1974 in

---

divert to redirect attention; to distract

Protesters angry about Watergate confronting President Richard M. Nixon in Michigan

Moscow; and the administration's efforts to secure a general peace in the Middle East following the Yom Kippur War of 1973.

The revelations from the Watergate tapes, combined with actions such as Nixon's firing of Watergate special prosecutor Archibald Cox, badly eroded the president's standing with the public and Congress. Facing certain impeachment and removal from office, Nixon announced his decision to resign in a national televised address on the evening of August 8, 1974. He resigned effective at noon the next day, August 9, 1974. Vice President Ford then became president of the United States. On September 8, 1974, Ford **pardoned** Nixon for "all offenses against the United States" which Nixon "has committed or may have committed or taken part in" during his presidency. In response, Nixon issued a statement in which he said that he regretted "not acting more decisively and **forthrightly** in dealing with Watergate." ❖

pardoned relieved or released another from potential legal consequences and punishments linked to one's actions
forthrightly honestly and directly

Influential Lives

Race Antagonisms

excerpt from Peking Dust: China's Capital During World War I
by Ellen N. La Motte

It is a crisp, cold morning, but nothing to what it will be, they tell us, when the autumn is over, and the bitter winter settles down upon North China. After all, come to think of it, we are abutting on two extremely Northern provinces, Manchuria and Mongolia, and these adjoin Siberia, which all the world knows is cold. So this sharp October day, with its brilliant blue sky and hard, glittering sunshine, is only a foretaste of the weather that will come later.

To-day we went into the Chinese City and visited a native department store. At the best speed of our **rickshaw**-boys we passed out of the Chi'en Men, the principal gate, and once beyond the towering, embattled wall that separates the Chinese from the Tartar City, we lost ourselves in the maze of narrow, winding streets that open on all sides from the main road leading from the Chi'en Men, which, by the way, has been in the possession of the American troops since the Boxer uprising. In the narrow hutungs our progress was slow; we literally shoved our way through crowds of rickshaws and thousands of pedestrians, and as there are no sidewalks, we were alternately scraping

---

antagonism aggression and opposition to something
rickshaw a vehicle, similar to a bicycle with three wheels, with room for passengers in the back

Peking cart

the walls and shop fronts on one hand, or locking wheels
with Peking carts on the other, and feeling the warm breath
of a camel or donkey down our necks whenever the traffic
brought us to a halt. Finally our boys stopped before a
large building about three stories high, emblazoned with
gold dragons, and with gorgeous red and yellow banners
and flags all over the front of it. It stood some distance
back from the street, and the wide courtyard in front
was filled and crowded with the carts and carriages of the
high-class women who had gone inside to shop.

I have already told you that Chinese horses can't
be driven; they must be led along with great show and

shouting. Well, when they stop they can't even be trusted to stay in harness; they must be unharnessed and removed to a place of safety. Therefore the courtyard of this department store presented a **unique** appearance, filled with twenty or thirty Peking carts, empty, tilted back on their haunches, with shafts gaping toward heaven. Also, the horses had been removed from innumerable little coupés of ancient date, with the **superstructure** all of glass, so that the occupant within is completely visible from all sides, like a fish in an aquarium.

Horses and mules, in gorgeous, glittering harness, were carefully stood apart, or were being led up and down in the crowded courtyard to cool off. Though why cool off, after a dash through the streets at two miles an hour or less, I couldn't see. However, here they all were,—great, high white horses, shaggy Mongolian ponies, and magnificent mules, the latter by far the most superb animals I've ever seen. I am not much at heights, but the mules were enormously tall, enormously heavy, very beautiful beasts, white, red, yellow, and black, and sleek with unlimited polishing and grooming. They were clad—that's the only word—in heavy, barbaric harness, mounted with huge brass buckles, and in some cases the leather was studded with jade, carnelian, and other semi-precious stones.

....

unique one-of-a-kind; unusual
superstructure a structure built on top of another

Fruit stall in the bazaar

Style? There's nothing on **Fifth Avenue** to touch it. Do you think a ten-thousand-dollar automobile is handsome? It's nothing to a Peking cart, with its huge, sleek mule and glittering harness. I tell you, the Chinese have the style of the world; the rest of us are but imitators. In comparison, our motors are merest upstarts. But you must picture a Peking cart, of beautifully polished wood, natural color, and a heavy wooden body covered with a big blue hood. The owner rides inside, on cushions, and on each shaft

Fifth Avenue a major roadway in the center of Manhattan, famous for its fashionable stores; sometimes called the most expensive street in the world

sits a servant, one to hold the reins, the other to yell and jump off and run forward to press his weight on the shaft to lessen the jar to the occupant whenever a bad bit of road presents itself. They say that this old custom, due to the discomfort and jolting of the springless carts, is the reason why the horses are not trained to round corners or go over bad bits of road alone. From time **immemorial** it has been the duty of the groom to run forward and throw his weight on the shafts to lessen the jolts; therefore he is the real, the important driver. In front of the blue-linen hood hangs a curtain, and the two side windows are also carefully curtained, with screens which permit the occupant to see out but not to be seen from without. Thus do high-class **mandarins** protect themselves, save themselves from having to descend whenever they meet a mandarin of equal or higher rank and prostrate themselves in the dust before him. Also, the longer the axle, the further it projects beyond the hub of the wheel, the higher the rank of the owner; it denotes his right to occupy the road. The rims of the wheels are spiked: big nails project all round, indicating the mandarin's right to tear up the road. It's all splendid and barbaric; no **mawkish** sentiment about it.

So we entered the department store through rows and rows, very neat and orderly, of upturned carts and

....

immemorial ancient; older than can be remembered
mandarins elite public officials in China
mawkish sappy or overly sentimental

antiquated coupés, and mules and horses and a courtyard full of liveried servants. Inside, it still looked barbaric, with its magnificent display of rich silks and furs. Great skins of tiger, panther, leopard, wildcat, sable, were hanging in profusion on all sides, interspersed with costly embroideries, wonderful **brocades**, and all the magnificence and color of the gorgeous East.

It was the idea of Kwong, our pet rickshaw-boy, to bring us here and we soon found that foreigners were not expected and not wanted. No one of the **suave** shop attendants could speak English, nor did they make the slightest attempt to wait on us. We wandered round, rather desolate, followed by looks of curiosity and **disdain** on the part of the clerks, and the wholly undisguised amusement and contempt of the high-class Chinese and Manchu women, who, with their liveried servants, were making the rounds of the various floors. In the store it was noisy and cheerful, the atmosphere cold and close except in the neighborhood of a few big red-hot stoves, which gave forth a local heat. Chinese women, not high-class, attired in satin trousers, sat about at small tables drinking tea and smoking cigarettes, tea and cigarettes being furnished free at innumerable little tables on every floor. As we passed, they giggled and nudged one another. Can't you imagine

....

brocades heavy woven fabrics, often embroidered with gold or silver threads
suave charming and sophisticated
disdain scorn or contempt

a Chinese lady in satin trousers passing through a great American department store and being remarked upon? To them we were equally queer, and they made no attempt to disguise the fact.

There was none of that **servile** deference one finds among the hotel servants and the rickshaw-boys, or of the extreme politeness of the upper-class Chinese whom we had met at the **legations** and elsewhere. To these people we were nothing but foreigners, and down at heart foreigners excite nothing but amusement or hostility. That conservative, gossiping throng of Orientals had a good, firm opinion of us, and it wasn't complimentary. We were interlopers and intruders, and had no business in that *pukkah* Chinese shop. We were glad to get out and to make our purchases in some kindlier atmosphere.

How can I reconcile this impression with previous ones, of the docility and servility we had previously encountered? Docility and subserviency are necessary in dealing with the conquering foreigner, but in such places and on such occasions when those qualities are not required, we get an impression of the real feelings of the Chinese. I believe they feel toward us very much as we should feel toward them, or toward any other nation that claimed us as a vassal state. For one country to be under the "influence" of another,

....

servile being overly willing to serve; having the characteristics of a slave or servant
legations referring to both diplomats that serve in a foreign country, and the office or residence of those diplomats

View of Peking, looking north, toward Forbidden and Imperial Cities

for any nation to assert a **"benevolent protectorate"** over another, is to engender the hostility of the state so patronized. Very well, it stands to reason. Foreigners have been patting China on the head for a long time, and repeated pats don't always produce a callous; sometimes they produce profound irritation.

This country is so enormous, so chaotic, one is so aware of the strength underlying its calm, **submissive** exterior, that one feels that some day this **latent** strength will break through and disclose itself. In trying to describe all these feelings at random, day by day as they come, I am not

....

benevolent kind
protectorate a region that is controlled by, and under the protection of, another country
submissive meek and obedient
latent hidden

Village outside walls of Peking

trying to sort them out and classify them and present them in an orderly manner. You must see them with me, and feel them with me from day to day, and do your own thinking later. That English boy on the boat coming over to China told us this. We asked him if he had enjoyed his vacation in Japan.

"Not much," he replied. "I don't care for the Japanese; they don't compare with the Chinese."

"What's the difference?" I asked.

He pondered a moment.

"I'll sum it up for you like this," he answered. "In Japan they treat you as an equal; in China they treat you as a superior."

That's it, I believe. Race antagonism all the way through. China is a conquered country. She doesn't dare show resentment or insist upon equality. Whatever her private opinion may be, she is helpless, and she must treat her conquerors with **deference** as superiors. But Japan has never been conquered by the foreigner. She is the only nation among all the nations of the Orient that has never been trodden underfoot by the European. She has never been **subjugated** and never been drugged. And, curious coincidence, she has reached a level with the foremost powers of the world, and holds the rank of a first-class nation. All this without having had the blessings of European civilization conferred upon her by a conqueror! She has snatched here and there, has imitated, even excelled, certain qualities and propensities of the white man, but has never been **blighted** by having Western civilization forced upon her. That's the rub. Japan is a striking example to the rest of Asia; her success is a striking commentary on the value of independence. She has attained eminence without the assistance of the great powers. And of the value of this assistance, conferred by the great powers upon the other nations of Asia— enough said. ❖

---

deference humility and respect
subjugated conquered or brought under another's control
blighted damaged or spoiled

President Barack Obama's State of the Union Address

January 28, 2014

Mr. Speaker, Mr. Vice President, Members of Congress, my fellow Americans:

Today in America, a teacher spent extra time with a student who needed it and did her part to lift America's graduation rate to its highest levels in more than three decades.

An entrepreneur flipped on the lights in her tech startup and did her part to add to the more than eight million new jobs our businesses have created over the past four years.

An autoworker fine-tuned some of the best, most fuel-efficient cars in the world and did his part to help America wean itself off foreign oil.

A farmer prepared for the spring after the strongest five-year stretch of farm exports in our history. A rural doctor gave a young child the first prescription to treat asthma that his mother could afford. A man took the bus home from the graveyard shift, bone-tired but dreaming big dreams for his son. And in tight-knit communities all across America, fathers and mothers will tuck in their kids, put an arm around their spouse, remember fallen comrades, and

President Barack Obama delivering the State of the Union address to a joint session of Congress, January 28, 2014

give thanks for being home from a war that, after twelve long years, is finally coming to an end.

Tonight, this chamber speaks with one voice to the people we represent: It is you, our citizens, who make the state of our union strong.

And here are the results of your efforts: The lowest unemployment rate in over five years; a rebounding housing market. A manufacturing sector that's adding jobs for the first time since the 1990s. More oil produced at home than we buy from the rest of the world—the first time that's happened in nearly twenty years. Our deficits—cut

deficits amounts by which an organization's expenses exceed its income by more than half. And for the first time in over a decade, business leaders around the world have declared that China is no longer the world's number one place to invest; America is.

That's why I believe this can be a breakthrough year for America. After five years of grit and determined effort, the United States is better-positioned for the twenty-first century than any other nation on Earth.

The question for everyone in this chamber, running through every decision we make this year, is whether we are going to help or hinder this progress. For several years now, this town has been consumed by a **rancorous** argument over the proper size of the federal government. It's an important debate—one that dates back to our very founding. But when that debate prevents us from carrying out even the most basic functions of our democracy—when our differences shut down government or threaten the full faith and credit of the United States—then we are not doing right by the American people.

As president, I'm committed to making Washington work better, and rebuilding the trust of the people who sent us here. And I believe most of you are, too. Last month, thanks to the work of Democrats and Republicans, Congress finally produced a budget that undoes some of last year's severe cuts to priorities like education. Nobody got everything they wanted, and we can still do more to

rancorous bitter, unfriendly, resentful

invest in this country's future while bringing down our deficit in a balanced way. But the budget compromise should leave us freer to focus on creating new jobs, not creating new crises.

And in the coming months, let's see where else we can make progress together. Let's make this a year of action. That's what most Americans want—for all of us in this chamber to focus on their lives, their hopes, their aspirations. And what I believe unites the people of this nation, regardless of race or region or party, young or old, rich or poor, is the simple, profound belief in opportunity for all—the notion that if you work hard and take responsibility, you can get ahead.

Now, let's face it: That belief has suffered some serious blows. Over more than three decades, even before the Great Recession hit, massive shifts in technology and global competition had eliminated a lot of good, middle-class jobs, and weakened the economic foundations that families depend on.

Today, after four years of economic growth, corporate profits and stock prices have rarely been higher, and those at the top have never done better. But average wages have barely budged. Inequality has deepened. Upward mobility has stalled. The cold, hard fact is that even in the midst of recovery, too many Americans are working more than ever just to get by—let alone to get ahead. And too many still aren't working at all.

Our job is to reverse these trends. It won't happen right away, and we won't agree on everything. But what I offer tonight is a set of concrete, practical proposals to speed up growth, strengthen the middle class, and build new ladders of opportunity into the middle class. Some require Congressional action, and I'm eager to work with all of you. But America does not stand still—and neither will I. So wherever and whenever I can take steps without legislation to expand opportunity for more American families, that's what I'm going to do.

As usual, our First Lady sets a good example. Michelle's Let's Move partnership with schools, businesses, and local leaders has helped bring down childhood obesity rates for the first time in thirty years—an achievement that will improve lives and reduce health care costs for decades to come. The Joining Forces alliance that Michelle and Jill Biden launched has already encouraged employers to hire or train nearly 400,000 veterans and military spouses. Taking a page from that playbook, the White House just organized a College Opportunity Summit, where already 150 universities, businesses, and nonprofits have made concrete commitments to reduce inequality in access to higher education—and to help every hardworking kid go to college and succeed when they get to campus. Across the country, we're partnering with mayors, governors and state legislatures on issues from homelessness to marriage equality.

The point is, there are millions of Americans outside Washington who are tired of stale political arguments and are moving this country forward. They believe, and I believe, that here in America, our success should depend not on accident of birth, but the strength of our work ethic and the scope of our dreams. That's what drew our **forebears** here. It's how the daughter of a factory worker is CEO of America's largest automaker; how the son of a barkeep is Speaker of the House; how the son of a single mom can be President of the greatest nation on Earth.... ❖

---

forebears ancestors

Influential Words

Homer:
The Poet for All Ages

*With the Bible and Shakespeare, the Homeric poems are the best training for life. There is no good quality that they lack: manliness, courage, **reverence** for old age and for the **hospitable hearth**; justice, **piety**, pity, a brave attitude toward life and death, are all **conspicuous** in Homer. Homer is a poet for all ages.*

—Andrew Lang

. . . .

reverence great respect; honor
hospitable friendly and welcoming to guests
hearth the place in front of a fireplace, used to stand for the idea of home
piety devotion—usually, religious devotion
conspicuous easily seen
Andrew Lang a nineteenth-century scholar and writer, whose works include a translation of the *Iliad* and the *Odyssey*

More than twenty-five hundred years ago, the people of a little Greek city somewhere on the shore of the Aegean Sea were gathered to celebrate the gods of their native land.

They met in the open air. The sun shone full on rocky cliffs, on the blue water of the bay, and on the glistening marble of temple and palace. The king and queen sat on thrones before the portico of the temple, surrounded by the elders and priests.

The crowd below was clothed in bright colors. Some of the youths wore the **laurel** wreaths they had won in the games and races of the morning. Now, in the quiet of the afternoon, all were waiting eagerly to hear a poet tell stories of the great deeds of their ancestors.

Imagine: a man of many years, serious and noble in bearing, comes forth from the temple, bearing a **lyre** in his hand. He kneels before the king, then rises and touches the strings of his lyre:

> *Sing, goddess, the wrath of Achilles, Peleus's son.*

His words rise over the market place, and a deeper silence falls over the people as the great story sweeps forth in the beautiful verses. The morning's races, the festival, the beauties of the city—all are forgotten as the listeners journey with the poet across the shining sea to fight with mighty Achilles on the windswept plains before the great

---

laurel the foliage of the laurel tree that the ancient Greeks used to crown victors
lyre a musical instrument like a small harp

city of Troy. The present grows dim, while the deeds and glories of the past grow bright, brought to life by the ringing verses of Homer's *Iliad* and *Odyssey*.

We do not know who Homer was, or when and where he lived. One legend says that long ago in Greece, a blind poet, Homer, wandered from city to city and earned his living by reciting poems, including the *Iliad* and the *Odyssey*, two great epics—which is the name for long poems that set forth in a grand manner the deeds of great heroes.

Some people believe that such a poet really lived, and that he composed the *Iliad* and the *Odyssey* himself and recited them in the cities where he stayed. Others believe that he had much less to do with the making of the poems. They say that the *Iliad* and the *Odyssey* belong to the time long before written history, when the stories of heroes' deeds were sung and recited, and so passed down by word of mouth from one generation to another. In this way, they believe, these great poems grew, being added to and gradually shaped through many years.

Whatever the source of the poems, however, they must have been recited for a good many years before they were finally written down. For writing was not known in Greece until the middle of the seventh century B.C., and the *Iliad* and the *Odyssey* go far back of that.

Probably we shall never really know the facts. But it is pleasing to think that the blind wandering poet had at least a hand in shaping these great poems. And it is wonderful that through all these hundreds of years, the fame of a man of whom so little is known has **persisted** so strongly. His fame seems to grow with the years, for as we learn more about the long-ago times, we appreciate more and more how great the *Iliad* and the *Odyssey* really are.

The *Iliad* tells of Achilles, the bravest of the Greeks, who **besieged** the city of Troy; and, of Hector, the bravest of Troy's defenders, who fell at last by the hand of his heroic foe. (The title, *Iliad*, comes from the word *Ilium*, which is the Greek name for Troy.)

The *Odyssey* tells of Odysseus (also known as Ulysses), one of the Greek chieftains at Troy. After the fighting ended, Odysseus wandered for many years and met many adventures before he finally reached his home and his faithful wife, Penelope.

These great epics were first recited on some such occasion as we have imagined, and since then they have never been forgotten. They tell of a past so distant that it is scarcely known except through their verses, and of gods who have long since ceased to be worshiped. Yet these epics are as fresh and alive today as when they were first chanted to the youths and maidens of that forgotten Grecian city.

---

persisted lasted; endured
besieged attacked and surrounded

The Greek Gods

If you have read Greek myths before, then you know that the actors in these stories include not only humans but also many gods.

The Greeks believed in many gods, male and female, all under the rule of the king of the gods, Zeus. They lived on a snow-capped peak called Mount Olympus, where they gathered from time to time in Zeus's banquet hall to discuss the affairs of men. The gods were thought to be immortal, and to have extraordinary powers, such as the ability to change into the shapes of different animals, or to fly, or to hurl thunderbolts from the sky.

And yet, despite their immortality and extraordinary powers, the Greeks imagined their gods living much as people do: eating, drinking, working, playing, and sleeping. Though the gods were supposed to reward good people and punish the bad, the Greeks told many stories in which the gods were cruel, jealous, selfish, **vengeful**, and in general displayed some of the worst human failings.

In the *Iliad*, which tells the story of a great war between the Greeks and the **Trojans**, the gods take sides, some favoring the Greeks, and others the Trojans. In the *Odyssey*, it is the wrath of the sea god, Poseidon, that throws

vengeful seeking revenge; eager to get even with someone
Trojans the people of the city of Troy

Odysseus off his course and keeps him from reaching home for many years.

After the Greeks, another great people rose to power, the Romans, in the land now called Italy. The Romans borrowed many ideas and customs from the Greeks, including their religion. The Romans worshiped the same gods as the Greeks, but called them by different names, as shown in the following table. This book refers to the gods by their Greek names, but in other books of myths, you will sometimes see the Greek names, and sometimes the Roman. ❖

Greek name	Roman name	Description
Zeus	Jupiter	king of the gods
Hera	Juno	wife of Zeus, queen of the gods
Athena	Minerva	goddess of wisdom
Aphrodite	Venus	goddess of love and beauty
Eros	Cupid	god of love, son of Aphrodite
Ares	Mars	god of war
Artemis	Diana	goddess of the moon and hunting
Hephaestus	Vulcan	god of fire and the forge
Hermes	Mercury	the messenger god
Demeter	Ceres	goddess of corn and growing things
Persephone	Proserpina	daughter of Demeter
Phoebus Apollo	Apollo	god of the sun, music, and poetry
Poseidon	Neptune	god of the sea
Hades	Pluto	god of the underworld

What Happened Before
the *Iliad*

When Homer's Iliad *opens, the war between the Trojans and Greeks, known as the Trojan War, is already underway. But how did the war begin? Who are the major characters on each side? Most of Homer's listeners would have known the answers to these questions from other stories already familiar to them. Here are some of those stories to help prepare you for the story of the* Iliad.

The Judgment of Paris

Far across the Aegean Sea that lies to the east of Greece, there once **flourished** a great city. This city was called Ilium by its own people, but in story and song it is known as Troy. It stood on a sloping plain some distance back from the shore, and was surrounded by high, strong walls that no enemy could **scale** or batter down. When the Trojans looked at the solid walls and noble buildings of their city, they boasted, "Ilium will stand forever."

King Priam, the ruler of this great city, seemed **favored** by the gods, for he had great wealth, the swiftest horses,

....

flourished thrived; prospered
scale to climb
favored treated with special regard or kindness

and many strong and brave sons. The strongest and bravest was named Hector, while the youngest and most beautiful was Paris.

Just before Paris was born, the **oracle** had **prophesied** that Priam's wife, Queen Hecuba, would give birth to a burning torch that would one day burn to the ground the strong walls and high towers of Troy. When the king and queen saw the beautiful face and noble features of the newborn babe, they could hardly believe that he was destined to be the ruin of his people.

But they also knew that to ignore the prophecies of the oracle would be unwise indeed. And so they faced a terrible choice: to await the certain destruction of their city, or to destroy the lovely child.

King Priam feared for the safety of his people. And so, with great sadness, he commanded that a shepherd should carry the babe to Mount Ida, and leave him there to die.

The shepherd obeyed the king unwillingly, and then returned to his home, heavy at heart, thinking of the helpless baby he had left alone on the mountain. At last he could bear the thought no longer and he **hastened** back. To his joy, he found the little prince still alive, so he carried him home in secret and kept him there as his own child.

....

oracle in mythology, a being who was believed to have knowledge from the gods
prophesied predicted
hastened hurried

Paris, as the boy was named, grew up with the shep herd lads, never suspecting that he was a king's son. He grew tall and straight, and so beautiful that his fame spread abroad. So he tended sheep on the mountainside while the time drew near when the prophecy was to be fulfilled.

Now it happened at this time in Greece that a great wedding was to be held between the king of a far-off country and a fair sea-**nymph**, Thetis. Kings and queens, and princes and princesses were invited to the wedding feast, and even the great gods came to do honor to Thetis.

Upon a high throne at the head of the hall sat mighty Zeus, and near him was proud Hera, his wife. There also were the shining sun god and his sister, the silver-footed moon goddess. Athena, the goddess of wisdom, came too, and Aphrodite, the goddess of beauty, and many others.

In the midst of the festivities, there entered suddenly Eris, the goddess of **discord**. She alone among the gods had not been invited, but this did not prevent her from making an unwelcome appearance. Before anyone had time to cry, "Beware!" she had cast a golden apple upon the table and then disappeared. Swift-footed Hermes seized the apple and read aloud the message inscribed upon it: *For the fairest.*

Not even Eris herself could have wished for greater results from her clever plan. At once **strife** arose in the hall

nymph in mythology, a beautiful maiden that lived in the forest, trees, or water
discord disagreement; conflict
strife bitter disagreement

of feasting, for each goddess thought that she deserved the apple. Most eager of all were Hera, Athena, and Aphrodite; before them, **mortal** maidens and lesser goddesses wisely became silent.

Among these three, the quarrel rose higher and higher, until Zeus commanded that a judge should decide the question once and for all, and let them have peace. He was unwilling to make the decision himself, for he knew that to choose one would be to risk the wrath of the other two. So he announced that he would appoint a judge who should declare which goddess was the fairest.

To Hera, Athena, and Aphrodite, he said, "Take yourselves with all due haste to Mount Ida. There you will find a fair young shepherd tending the flocks. Indeed, it is said that there is no man fairer. He shall decide to whom the apple belongs."

The three goddesses soon came to the mountainside where Paris tended his sheep, and handing him the golden apple, they asked to whom he would award it. The youth gazed upon them in wonder, quite unable to say which one was the most beautiful.

Each goddess in turn tried to win his favor by offering gifts. First Hera spoke, tempting him with the promise of a mighty empire and great wealth. Athena offered him glory and victory in war, and wisdom which would make him worthy of all honor. But then Aphrodite smiled upon

....

mortal a living being who will not live forever

him, and whispered close into his ear, "Choose me, fair youth, and I will give you the fairest woman in the world for your wife."

At her words, Paris forgot the longing for wealth and power that Hera's offer had sparked in him. He forgot his desire for victory and wisdom. To Aphrodite he gave the golden apple. This judgment of Paris was the beginning of many troubles. Little did he know that his choice meant ruin for his country, and for thousands of happy men and women.

Hera and Athena departed with hearts full of wrath. But Aphrodite smiled upon Paris and told him to **bide his time** until her promise should be fulfilled.

From that day Paris was restless and discontented. He no longer cared to tend his flocks upon the mountain, or to strive with the other young shepherds in the foot race and wrestling match.

One morning, he left his mountain home and went down to the city of Troy. On that day it chanced that great games were being held there, and Paris, taking part in the sports, put to shame all the other young men, for Aphrodite had given him godlike strength and swiftness.

King Priam, seeing Paris in action, asked, "Who is this noble youth? Of what family, and what place? I know him not, yet he seems to me almost as familiar as one of

....

bide his time to wait

my own sons." No one knew, so they began to ask about. And at length the old shepherd stepped forth from among the spectators and told the king that Paris was really the prince who had been left on the mountainside to die. Upon hearing this, Priam and Hecuba received their lost son joyfully, giving no thought to the prophecy that he should be the ruin of their city.

Paris came to dwell in the king's palace and returned no more to the shepherd's home. Honors were heaped upon him, and riches and power were at his command. Yet he never forgot the promise of Aphrodite nor ceased to long for its fulfillment.

The Beautiful Helen

At this time, one lady was by far the fairest in the world— Helen, the daughter of King Tyndarus. Every young prince heard of her beauty, and all desired to marry her.

Helen's father, King Tyndarus, was a wise man. When he saw kings and princes coming from afar to seek his daughter in marriage, he knew that only one of them could be made happy, and he did not wish the others to become his enemies. Therefore, before he chose a husband for Helen, as was the custom of the time, he gathered the **suitors** before him and spoke thus:

suitors men who court a woman with the hope of marrying her

"You do me great honor, my lords, but there is something which troubles me. You are many, and my daughter can have but one husband. How will it be when she makes her choice? Will I have only one friend and a score of enemies? My daughter would rather die unmarried than bring trouble upon me and my people. Therefore her **resolve** is this: you must swear a great oath that you will defend her and her husband, whomever she may choose, and that if he or she suffers any wrong, you will **avenge** it."

These words pleased the suitors, and they all pledged that they would defend Helen and her husband against all injury that might be done to them.

So Helen was wed to Menelaus, king of that part of Greece called Laconia, famed for the strength of its warriors. He took her to his palace in the capital city of Sparta. As for the disappointed suitors, they were men of honor, so they went home in peace, vowing to come to Helen's defense if ever they should be called.

Years went by, and at length Paris was sent by his father, King Priam of Troy, on a mission to Greece. He came to Sparta and was received with the hospitality **befitting** a prince from a faraway land. King Menelaus ordered a great feast, at which Paris was the guest of honor. That night,

....

resolve firm decision
avenge to get revenge for; to get even for
befitting worthy of; fit for

amidst the fine wine and pleasing conversation, Paris first looked upon the face of Helen, and Aphrodite whispered to him that this was the woman she had promised him for a wife.

Paris knew that he had never seen, and never could see, a lady so lovely and gracious as Helen. And so while Menelaus was away, and with Aphrodite's aid, he stole the beautiful Helen and de parted in his ships for Troy.

When Menelaus returned and learned what had happened, he was filled with grief and rage. He vowed to make war upon Troy and bring it to the dust. He called upon the kings and princes of Greece to remember their pledge and come to his aid.

This call was not to their liking, and some were **reluctant** to obey, but at last a great army was gathered together. One hundred thousand men and twelve hundred ships made ready to cross the sea to Troy to punish Paris and to restore Helen to Menelaus. Even the gods took sides. Hera and Athena had never for given Paris; therefore they favored the Greeks. But Aphro dite used her power to help the Trojans. Apollo, god of the sun, and Ares, god of war, also were on the side of the Trojans.

And so it was that a great army prepared for war. Determined to defend the honor of Greece, all **rallied** to the cause—all but two: Odysseus and Achilles.

reluctant hesitant; unwilling
rallied joined for a common purpose

Odysseus

One of the greatest of the suitors who had pledged themselves to Helen's defense was Odysseus. This noble king was famed alike for his brave deeds and for his sharp and active mind, always ready for any turn of events. For many years now, he had ruled his island home in peace. He had a fair young wife, Penelope, and a little son, Telemachus, whom he loved dearly. When the message came from Menelaus, asking his help in the rescue of Helen, he was at first unwilling to go.

It seemed to him a wild and foolish undertaking. It had been prophesied that if he went on this journey he should not return to his home for twenty years. He thought of the pain and trouble and warlike work of those twenty years, and looked on the loving faces of his wife and son, and chose to return no answer to Menelaus.

But the leaders of the Greeks were not willing to lose so good a warrior. When they received no reply to their message, Menelaus and some of his companions set out to journey to the land of Odysseus and find out the reason.

Odysseus, hearing that they had come, determined to trick them by pretending that he was out of his mind. He put on his richest garments, **yoked** an ox and a mule to his plow, and went out into his fields. As he plowed, he

....

yoked attached to a frame for pulling

scattered salt into the **furrows**, pretending that he thought it was seed.

But for once there was someone more clever than he. One of the followers of Menelaus suspected that Odysseus was playing a trick upon them, and decided to find out whether he was really mad or not. Just as the plow came opposite to him, the man suddenly took the baby son of Odysseus from the arms of the nurse and placed him on the ground directly in front of the ox. The sight of his son's danger made Odysseus forget his acting. He turned the plow aside and sprang forward to save his child. So Menelaus and his companions knew that the madness of Odysseus was a trick.

After this, Odysseus could no longer find any excuse for remaining at home. But though he had been unwilling to set out upon this war, he proved one of the greatest of its heroes. Indeed, it was not very long after this that he was able to do the Greeks a great service.

The Godlike Achilles

One of the fairest of the Greek youths was Achilles. He was the son of King Peleus and the sea-nymph Thetis, at whose wedding the apple of discord had fallen. His godlike beauty was like that of Thetis, his mother, and he had the

furrows shallow trenches left in a field after plowing

He turned the plow aside...to save his child.

WHAT HAPPENED BEFORE THE *ILIAD*

warlike strength of his kingly father. He was trained with the greatest care in all manly exercises, and showed greater strength and **valor** than any other youths of the land.

When Helen was stolen away and all Greece rose in arms to rescue her, Thetis was sad at heart. Zeus himself had told her that if Achilles went to this war, he would never return alive. Thetis knew well that this was true. She herself was immortal because she was a sea-nymph and belonged to the race of the gods; but Achilles was in part mortal.

When he was a baby, his mother had desired to make him immortal. So she had carried him to the dark **realm** of the underworld, and had bathed him there in the waters of the river Styx. The water of this river had such power that whatever it touched was safe from any **mortal** harm forever.

But there was one tiny spot upon his heel that had not been touched by the water. It was the place where Thetis had held him when she dipped him into the stream. She had forgotten to bathe it until she had returned to the earth once more, and it was then too late. This one spot upon his heel, she knew, would cause his death.

Before the first clash of arms sounded throughout Greece, Thetis had hurried Achilles away to an island

valor strength of will and great courage
realm kingdom
mortal fatal; causing death

across the sea. There she hid him, dressed as a girl, among the daughters of the king of that island.

The Greek leaders had been told by a trusted wise man that their war would not be successful unless the youthful Achilles accompanied them to Troy. The leaders, therefore, sought Achilles at his father's court; but he was not to be found. Odysseus then set out to discover where the youth was hidden.

At length he found out what Thetis had done, and he set out at once for the island. The boy was so well disguised that no one could have guessed that he was not a girl, but Odysseus devised a plan to discover him.

Dressing himself as a traveling merchant, he gained entrance to the king's garden, where the maidens were playing. From a large pack he carried, he brought forth golden rings, shining jewelry, and brightly colored scarves, which the maidens all examined eagerly—all except one tall maiden who stood aside and seemed to care little for them. Odysseus noted her **keenly** and determined to test her further. He drew from his pack a splendid sword, its blade sharp, strong, and gleaming in the sun. At once the tall maiden stepped forth and grasped the hilt and swung the sword with ease and delight.

Odysseus was now certain that this was the youth whom he sought. He announced his errand and called

....

keenly with sharp interest and insight

At once the tall maiden stepped forth and grasped the hilt.

upon Achilles to join the Greeks in their war against the Trojans. The boy, weary of his soft and easy life, readily agreed to accompany them.

He returned at once to his father's court to make ready. His mother, telling him of Zeus's prophecy, tearfully begged him to remain at home, but Achilles could not be moved. He **girded** on his shining armor and prepared himself for battle. Gathering his father's trusted warriors, he **bade** them make ready to go with him. They answered his summons with glad hearts, for they were proud to accompany this youth who was destined to perform mighty deeds.

But Thetis watched them depart in their great ships with a heavy heart. She feared that never again should she behold her godlike son. ❖

---

girded fastened
bade commanded; summoned; called to action

Stories from the *Iliad*

adapted from the retelling by Alfred J. Church

Prologue: The Long Siege

*Across the sea came a **host** of Greeks, armed for war and **bent** upon the **conquest** of Troy. They came because one of the princes of Troy, Paris, had done a great wrong to Greece when he had carried away the beautiful Helen, wife of Menelaus of Sparta. Crying out for **vengeance**, they came in a thousand ships, with sails and oars, and landed on the beach at the foot of the plain. They challenged the warriors of Troy to come out on the plain and meet them in battle.*

*Thus the **siege** was begun. For more than nine years the city of Troy was surrounded by determined foes. But the walls were strong, and the men who defended them were brave. Many fierce battles were fought outside the gates. Sometimes the victory seemed to be with the Greeks, sometimes with the Trojans—but neither could gain any great advantage over the other. The Trojans could not drive the invaders from their shores; the Greeks could not force their way past the strong walls into the city.*

---

host a great many
bent strongly determined
conquest the act of conquering, or overcoming, by military force
vengeance revenge; getting back at or getting even with someone
siege the act of surrounding a city or fortress for a long time, cutting it off from supplies, to force it to surrender

One hero after another was slain, now on this side, now on that. Many were the losses on both sides, and great the suffering and grief. But still the struggle went on.

*During the long siege, the Greeks sometimes took the battle beyond Troy to neighboring kingdoms friendly to the Trojans. Leaving part of their army to watch Troy, the rest the Greeks went to **plunder** other cities, taking food, cattle, wine, and sometimes women, whom they forced to work as slaves. All of these **spoils** were divided among the Greek **chieftains**, with the first choice going to the leader of all the Greek army, Agamemnon, the brother of Menelaus.*

After one of these raids, Agamemnon took for himself as a prize of war a girl named Chryseis. She was the daughter of Chryses, a priest of Apollo, the god who was worshiped in the plundered city.

It is at this point in the course of events of the Trojan War that Homer begins the Iliad.

---

plunder to use force to steal goods
spoils stolen items; loot or goods taken from an enemy, particularly during war
chieftains leaders of different groups

The Quarrel

This is the story of the anger of Achilles, that brought countless ills upon the **Achaeans**, from the day on which King Agamemnon and great Achilles first **fell out with** one another.

It happened that Chryses, priest of Apollo, came to Agamemnon and the other Greek chiefs. He had come to offer much gold to **ransom** his daughter, Chryseis. On his knees he begged them to take the gold and give him back the girl. "If you will do this," he said, "may the gods help you to take the city of Troy, and bring you back safe to your homes."

All the other chiefs were willing, but Agamemnon cried, "Away with you, old man. Do not linger here now and do not come again, or it will go hard on you, though you are a priest. As for your daughter, I will carry her back with me when I have taken Troy."

The old man left in great fear and sadness. He prayed to Apollo, and Apollo was angry that his priest should suffer such treatment. He came down from his palace atop Mount Olympus, shooting arrows among the Greeks, and each arrow carried deadly plague. For nine days the people

---

Achaeans another name for the ancient Greeks
fell out with quarreled; refused to have any dealings with
ransom to pay to release a captured person

died, and on the tenth day Achilles, the most **valiant** of the Greeks, called an **assembly**.

"Let us ask the **soothsayers** why Apollo is angry with us," said Achilles.

Then Calchas the soothsayer stood up. "You wish to know why Apollo is angry. I will tell you, but first you must promise to stand by me, for King Agamemnon will be angry when he hears what I have to say."

"Speak," said Achilles. "No man shall harm you while I live—nay, not Agamemnon himself."

Then Calchas said, "Apollo is angry because, when his priest came to ransom his daughter, Agamemnon refused him. Now, you must send back the girl, and take no money for her."

Then Agamemnon stood up and cried, "You are always the bearer of evil **tidings**! But so be it—I will give her up if I must, for I would not have the people die. But I will have some other share of the spoils. You must find me another prize instead, for I shall not be without one."

And Achilles answered, "How shall we find you another prize? Those we took from the cities have been awarded; we cannot take back prizes that have already been given. Therefore, give back this girl, and if ever Zeus grants us to

valiant brave and noble
assembly gathering; meeting
soothsayers persons who, the ancient Greeks believed, could predict the future
tidings news

sack the city of Troy, we will make it up to you three and four times over."

Then Agamemnon said, "Achilles, valiant though you be, you shall not thus outwit me. Are you to keep your own prize, while I sit tamely under my loss and give up the girl at your bidding? No—Achilles, I will come to your tent and take your own prize, the maiden Briseis."

The face of Achilles grew red with anger as he cried, "Never was there a king so shameless and greedy! I have no quarrel with the Trojans; I have been fighting in your cause and that of your brother, Menelaus. You leave me to fight while you sit in your tent at ease. But when the spoil is divided, you take the lion's share. And now you will take the little that was given to me. I will not **stay** here to be shamed and robbed. I will return home with my ships, for I will not stay here dishonored to gather gold and goods for you."

"Go," said Agamemnon, "and take your men with you. I have other chieftains as brave, who know that I am master here."

Then Achilles was mad with rage. He had half drawn his sword when the goddess Athena appeared beside him, though no one else in the assembly could see her. She caught Achilles by the hand and said, "I have come to

---

sack to plunder; to loot; in wartime, to take the valuables from a captured town
stay to stop; to halt

stay your rage. Use bitter words if you will, but do not draw your sword."

Achilles answered, "No matter how angry a man may be, he must do as you command." Then he thrust the heavy sword back into the **scabbard** and turned to Agamemnon.

"Drunkard, with the eyes of a dog and the heart of a deer! Never fighting in the front of the battle! You would rather go round and rob the prizes from any man who stands up to you. I swear to you, that from this time forth, you may look for Achilles but you shall not find him. When your men fall dying by the murderous hand of **Hector**, you shall not know how to help them, and you shall tear your heart with rage for the hour when you wronged the best of the Achaeans."

And Achilles went apart from his **comrades** and sat down upon the seashore, full of bitter anger.

Then Agamemnon went forth and took counsel with the chiefs, and soon the shrill-voiced **heralds** called the Greek host to battle. Many nations and many chiefs were there, but none that could compare with valiant Achilles— Achilles, whose very being ached for the clang of sword upon sword in battle, but who now sat apart and would not fight.

....

scabbard a sheath or cover for a sword
Hector son of King Priam of Troy, and Troy's greatest warrior
comrades fellow soldiers; companions heralds: messengers; announcers
heralds messengers; announcers

"I have come to stay your rage."

Hector and Andromache

Now the sons of Troy and their allies came forth from the gates of the city and set themselves in battle **array**. The most famous of their chiefs were Hector, son of Priam, bravest and best of all, and Aeneas, son of the goddess Aphrodite.

Across the wide plain that separated the shore from the high walls of Troy, the Greeks went forward to the battle silently and in order after their chiefs. But from the Trojan army came loud shouts and cries. On both sides the gods urged them on.

With Ares, the god of war, at his side, Hector dealt death and destruction through the ranks of the Greeks. Hera and Athena saw this and were angered. They passed down to earth and urged on the Greeks. With renewed strength, the Greeks fought so fiercely that, even without Achilles, they forced the Trojans to flee behind the walls of the city for safety.

When Hector passed through the gates into the city, he **bid** the mothers of Troy assemble in the temple of Athena to see if their prayers might calm the anger of the goddess. Andromache, the wife of Hector, saw him and hastened to meet him. With her was a nurse bearing Hector's only child, with a head like a star, so bright was his golden hair.

array arrangement; formation
bid told; requested

Hector smiled when he saw the child, but Andromache clasped Hector's hand and wept, saying:

"Oh, Hector, your courage will be your death. Some day all the Greeks will join together and rush upon you and slay you. It were better for me to die than to lose you, for I have no comfort but you. My father is dead, for the great Achilles killed him when he took our city. He killed him, but he did him great honor, for he would not take his arms for spoil, but burned them with him on the funeral **pyre**. And my seven brothers, they too are dead, for the great Achilles killed them all in one day. My dear mother, too, is dead. You are father to me, and mother, and brother, and husband also. Have pity, then, and stay there upon the city wall, **lest** you leave me a widow, and your child an orphan."

Hector answered her, "Dear wife, leave these things to me. I am not willing that any son or daughter of Troy should see me keeping away from battle. I hate the very thought of it; I must always be in the front."

Then Hector stretched out his arms to take the child. But the child drew back in the arms of his nurse with a loud cry, for he was frightened by his father's bronze helmet, which shone so brightly, and by the horsehair **plume**,

....

pyre a pile of materials, such as wood, used for burning a body as part of a funeral ritual
lest for fear that
plume a showy feather used for decoration

which nodded so awfully. Then father and mother laughed aloud. And Hector took the helmet from his head and laid it on the ground, and caught the child in his hands and kissed him, praying aloud:

"Grant, Father Zeus and all ye gods, that this child may be great among the sons of Troy; and may they say some day, when they see him carrying home the bloody spoils of war, 'He is an even greater man than his father!' And his mother shall be glad."

Then he gave the child to its mother; she clasped him to her and smiled a tearful smile. Her husband had pity on her and stroked her with his hand and said:

"Do not let these things trouble you. No man will kill me unless **fate** orders it; but no man may escape fate, be he cowardly or brave. Go, carry on your tasks at the **shuttle** and the **loom**, and give your maids their tasks. Let me take thought for the battle."

Then Hector took up his helmet from the ground, and white-armed Andromache went to her home, often turning back her eyes. And when she came to her home, she called all her maids together, and they wept and wailed for Hector as though he were already dead. And indeed, she thought in her heart that she should never see him coming home again safe from the battle.

But Hector went into battle with renewed fury, and everywhere the Greeks gave way before him.

Agamemnon's Appeal to Achilles

On the windswept plains before the high walls of Troy, the Greeks and Trojans clashed in battle. Many a brave warrior fell, leaving their bodies in bloody pools as food for dogs

....

fate destiny; to the ancient Greeks, the cause or will by which things happen
shuttle a part of a loom
loom a frame used to weave threads into cloth

and vultures, while their souls fled groaning to the dark realm of the dead.

Without Achilles, the Greeks could not stand against the strength and fury of Hector, who **slew** many and stripped them of their armor. The Greeks were pushed back to the shore, where the fighting raged by their ships.

And now the sun sank into the sea, and the night fell. The Trojans were angry that darkness had come and that they could not see any longer. But the Greeks were glad, for the night was a shelter to them, and gave them time to breathe.

Then Hector called the Trojans to gather at a place near the river, where the ground was clear of dead bodies. He stood in the middle of the people, holding in his hand a spear of some sixteen feet in length, with a shining head of bronze and a band of gold fastening the head to the shaft. When all were assembled, he spoke:

"**Hearken**, men of Troy, and ye, our allies who fight with us. I thought that today we should destroy the army of the Greeks and burn their ships, and go back to Troy and live in peace. But night has come and **hindered** us from finishing our work. Let us sit down, therefore, and rest and take a meal. Loose your horses from their chariots, and give them their food. Go, some of you, to the city, and fetch

---

slew killed
hearken to listen
hindered stood in the way of

cattle and sheep and wine and bread, that we may have plenty to eat and drink. I will say no more, but know this: tomorrow we will arm ourselves and drive these Greeks to their ships, and, if the gods are willing, burn their ships with fire. Tomorrow we shall surely bring ruin on the Greeks!"

So Hector spoke, and all the Trojans shouted with joy.

While the Trojans feasted, full of hope that they would soon be rid of their enemies, the Greeks were full of trouble and fear. No one among them was more sad at heart than King Agamemnon. He called his chiefs together. When they had gathered, not a word did they say, but looked sadly upon the ground. At last Agamemnon stood and spoke:

"Lords and rulers of the Achaeans, truly the great Zeus seems to hate me. Once he promised that I should take this city of Troy and return home in safety, but this promise he has not kept. I must go back to the place from which I came, without honor, and without many of the friends who came with me. Now, before we all **perish**, let us flee in our ships to our own land, for Troy is not ours to take."

And when the king finished this speech, the chiefs still sat saying not a word. Then old Nestor, wisest of all the Greeks, stood up in his place and said, "O king, Zeus has made you lord over many nations, and put many things

....

perish to die

into your hand. Therefore you are the more bound to listen to wise words, even though they may not please you. It was an evil day, O king, when you took the maiden Briseis from Achilles. The other chiefs did not **consent** to your deed, and I myself advised you not to do it. But you would not listen. Rather, you followed your own pride and pleasure, and shamed the bravest of your followers, taking from him the prize he had won with his own valor. Undo this evil deed, and make peace with this man you have wronged. Speak pleasant words to him, and give him noble gifts."

Agamemnon stood and said, "You have spoken truly, old sir. I acted as a fool that day—I do not deny it. For not only is Achilles a great warrior, but he is also dear to Zeus—and he who is dear to Zeus is worth armies of men. See how we are put to flight when he stands aside from the battle! This, surely, is the doing of Zeus. And now, as I did him wrong, so I will make amends. I will send back the maiden Briseis, and give him much more besides."

Three chiefs—Odysseus, Ajax, and Phoenix—were sent to take this message to Achilles. They went along the shore of the sea and to the camp of the Myrmidons, as the men of Achilles were called. There they found him playing on the harp, and as he played he sang a song about the valiant deeds done by heroes of old. By him sat his dear friend, Patroclus.

....

consent to agree

So the three chiefs came forward, led by Odysseus. When Achilles saw them, he jumped from his seat in astonishment. And Patroclus also rose, to do them honor.

"You are welcome, my friends," cried Achilles, "for though I am angry with the king, you are not the less my friends."

He bade them sit, and had wine and food brought to them. Patroclus poured the wine, strong and sweet, and gave each man his cup, and then prepared the feast. When they had had enough, Odysseus spoke:

"Hail, Achilles! Truly we have had no lack of feasting. But this is not a day to think of feasting, for destruction is close at hand. This very day the Trojans came near to burning our ships. Therefore have we come to ask that you no longer stand aside from the battle, but come and help us as of old. For truly our need is great. Hector rages furiously, saying that Zeus is with him. He vows that he will burn our ships with fire and destroy us all while we are choked with the smoke of the burning. Now, therefore, stir yourself, before it is too late. The king has sent us to offer you gifts, great and many, for the wrong that he did to you. So great and so many are they that no one can say that these are not worthy."

Odysseus described all the things Agamemnon had promised to give. And when he had finished, he said, "Be content: take these gifts. And if you have no thought for Agamemnon, yet have thought for the people who perish because you stand aside from the battle. Take the gifts, therefore, for by so doing you will have wealth and honor and love from the Greeks, and great glory also, for you will slay Hector. He is ready to meet you in battle, for he is proud and thinks there is none among the Greeks who can stand against him."

Achilles answered, "I will speak plainly, Odysseus, and say what is in my heart—for, as for that man who thinks one thing in his heart but says another thing with his tongue, he is hateful to me as death itself. Tell me now, what does it profit a man to be always fighting day after day? Even as a bird carries food to its **nestlings** till they are **fledged**, and never ceases to work for them, while she is herself but ill fed, so has it been with me. I took twelve cities to which I traveled in ships, and eleven to which I went by land, and from all I carried away much spoil. All this I brought to King Agamemnon, and he, who all the time stayed safe in his tent, gave a few things to me and others, but kept the greater part for himself. And then what did he do? He left to the other chiefs that which he had given them, but what he had given me, he took away. So, let him not ask me any more to fight against the Trojans. There are other chiefs whom he has not wronged and shamed; let him go to them to keep away the devouring fire from the ships. As for me, neither with Hector nor with any of the sons of Troy will I fight again. Tomorrow I will store my ships with food and water and launch them on the sea."

So **vehement** was Achilles that his listeners sat silent. Then Achilles continued, speaking quietly:

nestlings baby birds
fledged grown up and ready to fly
vehement forceful; intense

"Often in time past I have thought to marry a wife, to settle down in peace. For long ago, my mother, Thetis of the sea, said to me, 'My son, two destinies lie before you, and you may choose only one. If you stay in this land and fight against Troy, then you will never go back to your own land but will die in your youth. Only your name will live forever. But if you will leave this land and go back to your home, then you shall live long, even to old age, but your name will be forgotten.' Once I thought that fame was a better thing than life; but now my mind is changed, for indeed my fame is taken from me, since Agamemnon has put me to shame before all my people."

When Ajax heard this, he rose and said, "Let us go. We shall do no good here today. Achilles **cherishes** his anger and cares nothing for his comrades or his people. One man will take the price of blood from another, even though he has slain a brother or a son. He takes the gold and puts away his anger. But this man keeps his anger, and all for the sake of a girl. What he desires, I do not know. Surely he seems to lack reason."

Achilles answered, "You speak well, great Ajax. Nevertheless, the anger is yet hot in my heart, because Agamemnon put me to shame before all the people. But go, and take this message: I will not arise to do battle with the Trojans till Hector shall come to these tents and seek to

....

cherishes cares for deeply; nurtures

set fire to my ships. But if he shall do this, then I will arise, and I will stop him, however eager he may be for the battle."

So the messengers departed to carry the words of Achilles to King Agamemnon.

The Arming of Patroclus

Patroclus, of all men the dearest friend to Achilles, had been moved by the words of Odysseus and Ajax. He knew that the Greeks were **in sore need of** Achilles and his troops, and that the very sight of Achilles in his shining armor would strike terror into the hearts of the Trojans. So he went to his friend and said:

"Be not angry with me, great Achilles, for the Greeks are in great trouble. Many of the bravest are wounded, while you stand apart with your anger. If you will not go to battle, let me go, and your men with me. Let me put on your armor; so shall the Trojans be frightened, thinking that Achilles is in the battle, and the Greeks shall have a breathing space."

Achilles answered, "I said that I should not fight again till the Trojans should bring the fire near to my own ships. But now, as I see the people are in great need, it is time

....

in sore need of greatly needed

to give help—for I see the Trojans are gathered about the ships, while the Greeks scarcely have room to stand between their enemies and the sea. Go you, then, and put on my armor, and lead my people to the fight. Go and keep the fire from the ships. But when you have done this, come back and fight no more with the Trojans. Mind me: when you feel the joy of battle in your heart, do not be over-bold. When you have driven the Trojans from our ships, do not pursue them. Do not go near the wall of Troy, lest a god meet and harm you."

As they talked, the men of Troy set torches to the ships, and a great flame shot up to the sky. When Achilles saw it, he cried, "Hasten, Patroclus, for I see the fire rising from the ships. Put on my armor, and I will call my people to the war."

So Patroclus put on the armor—breastplate and shield and helmet—and bound upon his shoulder the silver-studded sword, and took a mighty spear in his hand—though not the great Pelian spear, which no man could **wield** but Achilles. Then he mounted the chariot of Achilles, drawn by the mighty horses that were a gift from Zeus himself.

While he did this, Achilles called his Myrmidons to battle. Fifty ships had he brought to Troy, and in each there were fifty men. To them he said, "Forget not the bold words that you spoke against the men of Troy, complaining that

----

wield to handle with skill

The men of Troy set torches to the ships.

I kept you from the battle against your will. Now you have your wish."

So the warriors went to battle in close array, helmet to helmet and shield to shield, close as the stones with which a builder makes a wall. And Patroclus, in the armor of Achilles, went in front.

Then Achilles went to his tent and took from his chest a great cup which Thetis, his mother, had given him. No man except Achilles drank from that cup, and he poured out of it offerings to no god but Zeus. First he cleansed it; then he washed his hands, and, standing before his tent, poured out wine to Zeus, saying, "O Zeus, I send my comrade to this battle. Make him strong and bold, and give him glory, and bring him home safe to the ships, and my people with him."

So he prayed, and Zeus heard his prayer: part he granted, but part he would deny.

When Patroclus came to the battle and the men of Troy beheld him, they thought that Achilles had forgotten his anger and come forth. Then the men of Troy turned to flee, and many chiefs fell by the spears of the Greeks.

But there were some among the Trojans and their allies who would not flee. Among these was Sarpedon, who came from a city far beyond Troy. When he saw his comrades flying before Patroclus, he cried aloud, "Stand now and be of good courage! I myself will try this great warrior and see what he can do." Then he flung his spear at Patroclus.

The spear flew wide of the mark. Then Patroclus flung his spear and it struck Sarpedon even through the heart. From his chariot, he fell, as a pine or a poplar falls on the hills before the woodsman's ax. And as he fell, he cried out, "**Suffer not** the Greeks to spoil me of my arms." And so saying, he died.

Hector and the men of Troy were much troubled, for among the allies there was none braver than Sarpedon.

....

suffer not do not allow

So they charged and drove back the Greeks from the body. The Greeks charged again in their turn. No one would have known the great Sarpedon as he lay in the middle of the **tumult**, so covered was he with dust and blood. At last the Greeks drove back the Trojans from the body and stripped it of its arms; but the body itself they did not harm, for at the bidding of Zeus, Apollo came down and carried it from the **fray**, and gave it to Sleep and Death that they should carry it to the homeland of the fallen warrior.

Then Patroclus, forgetting the command of Achilles that he return at once after driving the Trojans from the ships, thought in his heart, "Now shall I take the city of Troy." He rushed ahead across the plain until he came to the very gates of the city. Three times he scaled the wall, and three times did Apollo push him back. When Patroclus climbed for the fourth time, Apollo cried to him in a **dreadful** voice, "Go back, Patroclus! It is not for you to take the great city of Troy, no, nor even for Achilles, who is a far better warrior than you." Patroclus went back, for he feared the anger of the god. But though he thought no more of taking the city, he raged no less against the Trojans.

Then Apollo stirred up the spirit of Hector. Leaping into his chariot, Hector urged the Trojans on. "We will see whether we can drive back this Patroclus," he said,

---

tumult commotion; confused uproar
fray fighting
dreadful causing great fear

"for it must be he—Achilles he is not, though he wears his armor."

When Patroclus saw them coming, he took a great stone from the ground and cast it into the air. The stone struck the charioteer full on the helmet. As the man fell head first from the chariot, Patroclus laughed aloud and cried,

"Who would have thought that there would be such skillful divers in the city of Troy?"

Three times did Patroclus charge into the ranks of the Trojans, and each time he slew nine warriors. But when he charged for the fourth time, Apollo stood behind him and struck him such a great blow on the neck that his eyes grew dim. The helmet fell to the ground, and the horsehair plume was soiled with dust. Never before had that headpiece, the helmet of Achilles, touched the earth. The spear also that he carried in his hand was broken, and the shield fell from his arm, and the breastplate on his body was loosened. Then, as he stood confused and without defense, one of the Trojans wounded him in the back with his spear. Patroclus turned to flee, but Hector thrust with his spear and hit him above the hip.

Patroclus fell to the ground, and Hector stood over him and cried, "Did you think to spoil our city, Patroclus? Instead, you are slain, and the great Achilles cannot help you."

But Patroclus answered, "You boast too much, Hector. It was not you that slew me, but Apollo. And mark you, death is close to you by the hand of the great Achilles."

Hector replied, "Why do you prophesy my death? It may be that, as I have slain you, so shall I slay the great Achilles." So Hector spoke, but his words went unheard by Patroclus, who lay dead.

How the Death of Patroclus Roused Achilles

Fierce was the fight about the body of Patroclus, and many heroes on both sides fell. First to fall was the man who had wounded Patroclus in the back, for when he came near to strip the dead man of his arms, Menelaus rushed at him with his spear and slew him. Then Hector came and stood over the body, and Menelaus did not dare to go against him, for he knew he was no match for him in fighting. So Hector stripped off the arms of Patroclus, the arms which

roused moved to action

Achilles had given him to wear, and put them on himself. When Zeus saw him do this, he was angry, and said, "These arms will cost Hector **dear**."

The battle for the body of Patroclus grew fiercer and fiercer. For the Greeks said, "It were better that the earth should open and swallow us alive than that we should let the Trojans carry off the body of Patroclus." And the Trojans said, "Now if we must be slain fighting for the body of this man, be it so, but we will not yield."

As they fought, the horses that pulled the chariot of Achilles, which Patroclus had driven into battle, stood apart and would not move. The tears rushed from their eyes, for they loved Patroclus, and they knew that he was dead. Still they stood, and they would neither enter the battle nor turn back to the ships. And the Greeks could not move them with the lash or with threat or with gentle words. They stood, their heads drooped to the ground, the tears trickling from their eyes, their long manes trailing in the dust.

When Zeus saw them, he pitied them. And he said, "It was not wise that I gave you, immortal creatures as you are, to a mortal man, for of all things that live and move upon the earth, surely man is the most miserable. But Hector shall not have you. It is enough for him—yea, it is too much—that he should have the arms of Achilles."

dear at a high price

Then the horses moved from their places and obeyed their driver as before. And Hector could not take them, though he longed to do so.

All this time, as the battle raged around the body of Patroclus, a messenger made his way to Achilles. He found the great warrior by the door of his tent. Then he said, weeping as he spoke, "I bring bad news for you. Patroclus is dead, and Hector has his arms, but even now the Greeks and Trojans are fighting for his body."

Achilles threw himself upon the ground and took the dust of the plain in his hands and poured it on his head. He wept and tore his hair. But his mother, Thetis, heard his cry, and from the depths of the sea she came and laid her hand on his head and asked, "Why do you weep, my son?"

Achilles answered, "My friend Patroclus is dead, and Hector has the arms which I gave him to wear. I care not to live, except to avenge his death."

Then Thetis said, "My son, do not speak so. You know that when Hector dies, then is the hour near when you also must die."

Then Achilles cried in great anger, "I would that I could die this hour, for I sent my friend to his death—and I, who am greater in battle than all the Achaeans, could not help him. Cursed be the anger that sets men to strive against one another, as it made me strive with Agamemnon. As for my fate—what does it matter? Let it come when it may, as long as first I have my vengeance upon Hector. Therefore, mother, do not seek to keep me back from the battle."

Thetis answered, "Be it so, my son. But you cannot go into battle without arms. Tomorrow I will go to Hephaestus and have him make new arms for you."

While they talked the men of Troy drove the Greeks back more and more. Then the body of Patroclus would have fallen to the Trojans, had not Zeus sent a messenger to Achilles.

"Rouse thee, Achilles," said the messenger, "or the body of Patroclus will be a prey for the dogs of Troy."

Achilles answered, "How shall I go?—for arms have I none, nor do I know of any man's I might wear."

The messenger replied, "Go only to the trench and show yourself; then the Trojans will draw back, and the Greeks will have a breathing space."

So Achilles ran to the trench. And Athena put her great shield about his shoulders, and set a circle of gold above his head that shone like a flame of fire. Then he cried out, and his voice was as the sound of a trumpet. It was a sound terrible to hear, and the hearts of the men of Troy were filled with fear. They stood in dumb amaze when they saw above his head the flaming fire that Athena had **kindled**. The very horses were frightened and started so that the chariots clashed together.

---

kindled lit; set ablaze

Three times Achilles shouted across the trench, and three times the Trojans fell back. Then the Greeks took up the body of Patroclus and put it on a **bier** and carried it to the tent of Achilles, as Achilles himself, weeping, walked by the side of the body.

They washed the body of Patroclus, and put ointment into the wounds, and laid it on a bed, and covered it with linen from head to foot, and over this draped a white robe. And all through the night there was great mourning for Patroclus in the camp of the Greeks.

The Making of the Arms

Thetis, immortal mother of Achilles, went to the house of Hephaestus, the god of all those who worked in gold and silver and iron. She found him busy at his work, making **cauldrons** for the palace of the gods on Mount Olympus. These cauldrons had golden wheels beneath them with which they could move on their own power into the chambers of the palace and back out again, as the gods willed.

When Hephaestus heard that Thetis wished to see him, he smiled and said, "Truly, there could be no guest more welcome than Thetis. When my mother cast me out from

---

bier a frame on which to carry a dead body
cauldrons large kettles

her because I was lame, it was Thetis and her sister who received me in their house under the sea. Nine years I dwelt with them, and hammered many a pretty trinket for them in a cave close by. Truly, I would give my life to serve Thetis."

Then he put away his tools, washed himself, and came into the house. To Thetis he said, "Tell me all that is in your mind, for I will do all that you desire if only it can be done."

Then Thetis told of how her son Achilles had been shamed by Agamemnon, and of his great anger, and all that came to pass afterwards, and how Patroclus had been slain in battle, and how the arms were lost. Having told this, she said, "Hephaestus, make for my son, Achilles, I pray you, a shield and a helmet, and **greaves** for his legs, and a strong breastplate."

Hephaestus answered, "I will make for him such arms as men will wonder at when they see them." So he went to his **forge** and turned the **bellows** to the fire and bade them work, for they needed no hand to work them. And he put copper and tin and gold and silver into the fire to make them soft, and took the hammer in one hand and the tongs in the other.

First he made a shield, great and strong. On it he made an image of the earth and the sky and the sea, with the

....

greaves protective armor for the shins
forge a furnace where metal is melted and shaped
bellows a tool that pumps air, used by a blacksmith to feed a fire

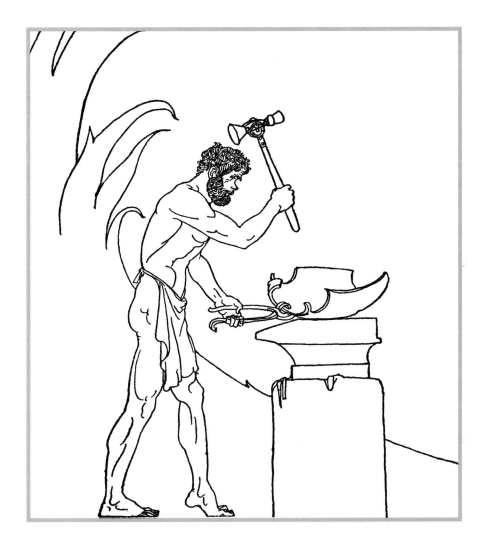

sun and the moon and all the stars. Also, he made images of two cities: in one city there was peace, and in the other city there was war. In the city of peace they led a bride to the house of her husband with music and dancing. But round about the city of war there was an army of besiegers, and on the wall stood men defending it. Also, the men of this same city had set an **ambush** by a river at a place where the cattle came down to drink. And when the cattle came down, the men that lay in ambush rose up quickly and took them, and slew the herdsmen. And the army of the besiegers heard the cry, and rode on horses, and came quickly to the river, and fought with the men who had taken the cattle.

Also, he made the image of one field in which men were plowing, and of another in which reapers reaped the corn; and behind the reapers came boys who gathered the corn in their arms and bound it in sheaves. At the top of the field stood the master, glad at heart because the harvest was good.

He made, too, the image of a vineyard, and through the vineyard there was a path, and along the path went young men and maids bearing baskets of grapes, and in the midst stood a boy holding a harp of gold, who sang a pleasant song. Also he made a herd of oxen going from the stalls to the pasture; and close by, two lions had laid hold of a great bull and were devouring it, while the dogs stood far off and barked.

He made as well the image of a dance of men and maids. The men wore daggers of gold hanging from silver belts, and the maids wore gold crowns round their heads. And round about the shield, he made the ocean, like a great river.

....

ambush a trap for an enemy; a sudden surprise attack

Also he made a strong breastplate, and a great helmet with a ridge of gold in which the plumes should be set, and greaves of tin for the legs. When he had finished all this work, he gave the armor to Thetis. She flew swift as a hawk to her son, and found him lying on the ground, weeping aloud, holding in his arms the body of Patroclus.

Catching her son by the hand, the goddess said, "Come now, let us leave. It was the will of the gods that he should die. But you must think about other things. Come, and take this gift from Hephaestus—armor of exceeding strength and beauty, such as no man has ever yet worn."

As she spoke, she placed the armor at the feet of Achilles. It shone so brightly that it dazzled the eyes of the Myrmidons. Achilles took up the arms, and his eyes blazed with fire, and he rejoiced in his heart. "Mother," he said, "these indeed are such arms as only the gods could make. Gladly will I put them on for the battle."

The Vengeance of Achilles

So Achilles gathered the Greeks for the battle, and his armor flashed like fire. On the wide plain between the shore and the high-walled city, the two armies gathered.

Then Apollo spoke to Aeneas, the son of Aphrodite and a Trojan nobleman, and among the Trojans second only to Hector in fame and valor. "Stand up against Achilles," said the god to the Trojan prince. "Drive straight at him with your spear, and do not fear his fierce words and looks."

So Aeneas came forth to meet Achilles. And Achilles said to him, "What do you mean by this, Aeneas? Do you think to slay me? Have the Trojans promised to make you their king if you **prevail** over me? You will not find it an easy task."

Aeneas said, "Son of Peleus, you will not frighten me with your words, for I also am the son of a goddess. Come, let us try who is the better of us two."

So he cast his spear, and it struck full on the shield of Achilles, and made so dreadful a sound that Achilles himself was shaken. But a shield made by a god could not be shattered by the spear of a mortal man. Indeed, it pierced the first and second layers, which were of bronze, but was stopped by the third, which was of gold, and touched not the last two layers, made of tin.

Now Achilles threw his spear. Easily it pierced the shield of the Trojan, and, though it did not wound him, it came so close that he was deadly frightened. Yet he did not flee, for when Achilles drew his sword and rushed at him, he took up a great stone from the ground to throw at him. Nevertheless he would certainly have been slain were it not for the help of the gods. For it was decreed that Aeneas and his children after him should reign over Troy in the years

---

prevail to triumph

to come. Therefore Poseidon, upon the order of Zeus, hid
Aeneas in a cloud of fog, then caught him up and carried
him away from the battle. But first he took Achilles's spear
from the shield and laid it at the hero's feet. As the fog
cleared, Achilles saw his spear and cried, "Here is a great
wonder. My spear that I threw I see lying at my feet, but the
man at whom I threw it, I see not. Truly this Aeneas must
be dear to the gods."

Then he rushed into the battle, slaying right and left. As the Trojans fled before Achilles, they came to the river Xanthus, and they leaped into it till it was full of horses and men. Achilles left his spear upon the bank and rushed into the water with only his sword. And the Trojans were like fishes in the sea when they flee from a dolphin: in rocks and shallows they hide themselves, but the great beast devours them **apace**.

Back and yet further back Achilles drove the men of Troy before him, closer and closer to the city walls. That hour the Greeks would have taken Troy, but Apollo saved it by drawing Achilles away from the city. And the way in which he saved the city was this. He put courage into the heart of Agenor, a Trojan chief, who stood by the gate waiting for Achilles. And when Achilles came near, Agenor threw his spear and struck his leg beneath the knee. But the strong greave turned aside the spear. Enraged, Achilles rushed to slay his attacker. But Apollo lifted Agenor from the ground and set him safely within the city walls.

Then Apollo took the form of Agenor, and fled before Achilles, and Achilles pursued him far from the walls of Troy. At last the god turned and spoke to him: "Why do you pursue me, swift-footed Achilles? Have you not yet discovered that I am a god, and all your fury is **in vain**? And now all the Trojans are safe within the city, and

---

apace swiftly; rapidly
in vain useless

you are here, far out of the way, seeking to kill one who cannot die."

In great wrath Achilles answered him, "You have done me wrong in drawing me away from the city, Great Archer. Had I the power, you would pay dearly for this cheat."

The Trojans were now safe in the city, refreshing themselves after all their **toil**. Hector alone remained outside the walls, standing in front of the gates of the city.

From the high wall, King Priam spied Achilles rushing toward the city. He cried to Hector, "Oh my son, come within the walls, for you are the hope of the city."

Then Queen Hecuba cried to him, "O Hector, my son, have pity. Come, I **beseech** you, inside the walls, and do not stand in battle against him."

But Hector was resolved to await the coming of Achilles and meet him in battle. And as he waited, he thought, "It is better to meet in arms and see whether Zeus will give the victory to him or to me."

Achilles approached, **brandishing** his great spear, and the flashing of his arms was like fire or the sun when it rises. When he saw this, Hector trembled. His nerve failed him, and he turned to run. Fast he fled from the gates, and fast Achilles pursued him. Past the watchtower they ran, past the wild fig tree, along the wagon road which

---

toil hard labor
beseech to beg
brandishing waving in a threatening manner

went about the walls. On they ran, one fleeing, the other pursuing. **Thrice** they ran around the city, but Apollo helped Hector, or he could not have held out against Achilles, who was swiftest of foot among the sons of men.

As they sat in their place on the top of Mount Olympus, the gods looked on. And Zeus said, "This is a **piteous** thing I see. My heart is grieved for Hector. See how the great Achilles is pursuing him! Come, let us discuss the matter. Shall we save him from death, or shall we let him fall by the spear of Achilles?"

Athena replied, "What is this that you propose? Will you save a man that the fates appoint to die?"

Then Zeus said, "So it must be, but it is a thing I hate."

All this time, Hector still fled, and Achilles still pursued. Then Athena flew down to Achilles and said, "This is your day of glory. Stand here and take breath, and I will make Hector meet you." So Achilles stood, leaning on his spear.

Then Athena took the shape of one of Hector's brothers, Deiphobus, and came near to him, and said, "My brother, Achilles presses you hard; but come, we two will stand against him."

Hector answered, "O Deiphobus, I have always loved you, and now I love you still more, for you alone have come to my help, while the rest remain within the walls."

---

thrice three times
piteous worthy of pity; pitiful

Then Hector turned to Achilles and cried out, "Three times have you pursued me round the walls and I dared not stand against you, but now I fear you no more. Only let us make this **covenant**: if Zeus gives the victory to me today, I will take your arms but return your body to the Greeks. Promise, therefore, to do the same with me."

Achilles frowned and said, "Hector, do not speak to me of covenants. Men and lions make no promises to each other, neither is there any agreement between wolves and sheep. Come, let us fight, that I may have vengeance for the blood of all my comrades whom you have slain, and especially for Patroclus."

Then he threw his great spear, but Hector saw it coming and avoided it, crouching on the ground, so that it flew above his head and fixed itself in the earth. But Athena snatched it up and gave it back to Achilles, though Hector did not see this.

"You have missed your aim, great Achilles," said Hector. "You shall not drive your steel into my back, but here into my breast, if the gods will it so. But now look out for my spear."

Then Hector threw his long-shafted spear. True aim he took, for the spear struck the very middle of Achilles's shield. It struck, but it did not pierce it, and bounded far away, for the shield was not made by the hand of man. Then Hector cried, "Deiphobus, give me your spear!"

covenant a formal agreement; a solemn promise

But Deiphobus was nowhere to be seen. Hector stood dismayed: he knew that his end was near. Then he said to himself, "The gods have brought my doom upon me. But if I must die, let me at least die doing such a deed as men will remember in the years to come."

He drew his mighty sword and rushed at Achilles. But Achilles charged to meet him, his shield before his breast, his helmet bent forward as he ran. The gleam of his spear-point was as the gleam of the evening star. Achilles well knew the one unprotected spot in the armor that Hector had taken from Patroclus. Into the spot where the neck joins the shoulder he drove his spear, and Hector fell in the dust.

Achilles drew his spear out of the body, and stripped off the bloody armor. All the Greeks came about the dead man, marveling at his strength and beauty. Looking at one another they said, "Surely this Hector is less dreadful now than in the day when he burned our ships with fire." ❖

Stories from the *Odyssey*

adapted from the retelling by Padraic Colum

Part 1
A Son's Adventures

The Visitor to Telemachus

This is the story of Odysseus, the most **renowned** of all the heroes the Greek poets have told us of—of Odysseus, and his long wanderings after the fall of the high walls of Troy. And this story of Odysseus begins with his son, the youth who was called Telemachus.

It was when Telemachus was a child of a month old that a messenger came from Agamemnon, the great king, bidding Odysseus betake himself to the war against Troy. Odysseus reluctantly **bade** good-bye to his infant son, and to his young wife, Penelope, and to his father, old Laertes. He bade good-bye to his house and his lands and to the island of Ithaca where he was king, and thereafter he took his sailors and his fighting men with him and he sailed away.

---

renowned celebrated; well-known; famous
bade said; told

The years went by and Odysseus did not return from Troy. After ten years the city was taken by the kings and princes of Greece, and the thread of war was wound up. But still Odysseus did not return. And now **minstrels** came to Ithaca with word of the deaths or the homecomings of the heroes who had fought in the war against Troy. But no minstrel brought any word of Odysseus. Ten years more went by. And now that infant son whom he had left behind, Telemachus, had grown up and was a young man of strength and purpose.

One day, as he sat sad and **disconsolate** in the house of his father, Telemachus saw a stranger come to the outer gate. There were many in the **court** outside, but no one went to receive the newcomer. Then, because he would never let a stranger stand at the gate without hurrying out to welcome him, and because, too, he had hopes that some day such a one would bring him **tidings** of his father, Telemachus rose up from where he was sitting and went to the gate at which the stranger stood.

"Welcome to the house of Odysseus," said Telemachus giving him his hand.

The stranger clasped it with a friendly clasp. "I thank you, Telemachus," he said, "for your welcome, and glad

....

minstrels in ancient times, singers of verses, often about heroes and their deeds
disconsolate unhappy; gloomy; dejected
court courtyard; open space enclosed by walls or buildings
tidings news

I am to enter the house of your father, the renowned Odysseus."

The stranger looked like one who would be a captain among soldiers. His eyes were gray and clear and shone wonderfully. In his hand he carried a great bronze spear. He and Telemachus went together through the court and into the hall. And when the stranger left his spear within the spearstand, Telemachus took him to a high chair and put a footstool under his feet.

He had brought him to a place in the hall where the crowd would not come. There were many in the court outside and Telemachus would not have his guest disturbed by questions or **clamors**. A handmaid brought water for the washing of his hands, and poured it over them from a golden **ewer** into a silver basin. A polished table was left at his side. Then other servants set down bread and dishes of meat with golden cups, and afterwards the maids came into the hall and filled up the cups with wine.

But the servants who waited on Telemachus and his guest were disturbed by the crowd of men who now came into the hall. They seated themselves at tables and shouted out their orders. Great dishes of meat were brought to them and bowls of wine, and the men ate and drank and talked

clamors loud noises
ewer a pitcher or jug

loudly to each other and did not **refrain** even from staring at the stranger who sat with Telemachus.

"Is there a wedding-feast in the house?" the stranger asked, "or do the men of your **clan** meet here to drink with each other?"

A flush of shame came to the face of Telemachus. "There is no wedding-feast here," he said, "nor do the men of our clan meet here to drink with each other. My guest, because you seem so friendly to my father's name, I will tell you who these men are and why they trouble this house."

Telemachus told the stranger how his father had not returned from the war of Troy although it was now ten years since the city was taken by those with whom he went. "Alas," Telemachus said, "he must have died on his way back to us, and I must think that his bones lie under some nameless channel of the ocean. Had he died in the fight at Troy, then the kings and princes would have made him a burial-mound worthy of his name and his deeds, and I, his son, would not be **imposed upon** by such men as you see here—men who are feasting and giving orders in my father's house and wasting the **substance** that he gathered."

"How come they to be here?" asked the stranger.

....

refrain to stop oneself from doing something
clan families descended from the same ancestor
imposed upon taken advantage of
substance goods; property

Telemachus told him about this also. When seven years had gone by from the fall of Troy and still Odysseus did not return, there were those who thought he was dead and would never be seen more in the land of Ithaca. Then many of the young lords of the land wanted Penelope, Telemachus's mother, to marry one of them. They came to the house to **woo** her for marriage. But she, ever hoping that he would return, would give no answer to them.

When he had told him all this Telemachus raised his head and looked at the stranger: "O my guest," he said, "wisdom and power shine out of your eyes. Speak now and tell me what I should do to save the house of Odysseus from ruin. And tell me too if you think it possible that my father should still be in life."

The stranger looked at him with his gray, clear, wonderfully shining eyes. "As I look at you," said the stranger, "I **mark** your head and eyes, and I know they are such a head and such eyes as Odysseus had. Well, being the son of such a man, and of such a woman as the lady Penelope, your spirit surely shall find a way of destroying those **suitors** who would destroy your house."

"Already," said Telemachus, "your gaze and your speech make me feel equal to the task of dealing with them."

....

woo to court; to seek the affection of
mark to take notice of
suitors men who court a woman with the hope of marrying her

"I think," said the stranger, "that Odysseus, your father, has not **perished** from the earth. He may yet win home through labors and **perils**. But you should seek for tidings of him. Hearken to me now and I shall tell you what to do.

"Tomorrow summon a council of all the chief men of the land of Ithaca, and stand up in that council and declare that the time has come for the suitors who **waste** your substance to scatter, each man to his own home. And after the council has been held, voyage to find out tidings of your father, whether he still lives and where he might be. Go to Sparta, to the home of Menelaus and Helen, and beg tidings of your father from them. And if you get news of his being alive, return. But if you learn that your father, the renowned Odysseus, is indeed dead and gone, then come back, and in your own country raise a great funeral mound to his memory. Then let your mother choose a good man to be her husband and let her marry him, knowing for a certainty that Odysseus will never come back to his own house. After that, you will have to punish those suitors who destroy the goods your father gathered and who insult his house by their presence. And when all these things have been done, you, Telemachus, will be free to seek out your own fortune: you will rise to fame, for I mark that you are

....

perished died
perils dangers
waste to weaken; to seriously injure

handsome and strong and most likely to be a wise and **valiant** man. But now I must **fare** on my journey."

The stranger rose up from where he sat and went with Telemachus to the outer gate. Telemachus said, "What you have told me I shall not forget. I know you have spoken out of a wise and a friendly heart."

The stranger clasped his hands and went through the gate. And then, as he looked after him Telemachus saw the stranger change in his form. He became first as a woman, tall, with fair hair and a spear of bronze in her hand. And then the form of a woman changed too. It changed into a great sea-eagle that on wide wings rose up and flew high through the air. Telemachus knew then that his visitor was an immortal and no other than the goddess Athena, who had been his father's friend.

Telemachus Speaks

When Telemachus went back to the hall, those who were feasting there had put the wine-cups from them and were calling out for the minstrel to come and sing some tale to delight them. As Telemachus went amongst them, one of the suitors said to another, "The guest who was with him has told Telemachus something that has changed

....

valiant brave and noble
fare to go; to travel

his **bearing**. Never before did I see him hold himself so proudly."

The minstrel came and the suitors called upon him to sing them a tale. And he sang of the return of the kings and princes from Troy, and of how some god or goddess put a trouble upon them as they left the city they had taken. And as the minstrel began the tale, Penelope, Telemachus's lady-mother, was coming down the stairs with two handmaids behind her. She heard the words he sang, and she stood still in her grief and drew her veil across her face. "Oh," she cried, "cease from that story that ever wastes my heart—the story that has brought me sorrow and that leaves me comfortless all my days!"

The minstrel would have ceased when Penelope spoke thus to him, but Telemachus went to the stairway where his lady-mother stood, and addressed her.

"My lady-mother," said he, "why should you not let the minstrel delight the company with such songs as the spirit moves him to give us? It is no blame to him if he sings of that which is sorrowful to us. As for you, my mother, you must learn to endure that story, for long will it be sung far and wide. And you are not the only one who is **bereaved**— many another man besides Odysseus lost the happy day of his homecoming in the war of Troy."

....

bearing manner; the way one carries oneself
bereaved sorrowful due to the loss of a loved one

Penelope, his lady-mother, looked in surprise at
the youth who spoke to her so wisely. Was this indeed
Telemachus who before had hardly lifted his head? And as
she looked at him again she saw that he carried his head—
that head of his that was so like Odysseus's—high and
proudly. She saw that her son was now indeed a man.

Penelope spoke no word to him, for a new thought had come into her mind. She turned round and went back with her handmaids to the chamber where her loom and her **distaff** were. And as she went up the stairway and away from them, her suitors muttered one to the other that she would soon have to choose one of them for her husband.

Telemachus turned to those who were standing at the tables and addressed them: "Suitors of my mother," he said, "I have a word to say to you. Let us feast now in peace, without any **brawling** amongst us, and listen to the tale that the minstrel sings to us. But tomorrow let us have a **council** made up of the chief men of this land of Ithaca. I shall go to the council and speak there. I shall ask that you leave this house and feast on goods that you yourselves have gathered. Let the chief men judge whether I speak in fairness to you or not. If you do not heed what I will say openly at the council, before all the chief men of our land, then let it be on your own heads what will **befall** you."

All the suitors marveled that Telemachus spoke so boldly. And one said, "Because his father, Odysseus, was king, this youth thinks he should be king by inheritance. But may Zeus never grant that he be king."

---

distaff a tool used for holding flax or wool when spinning thread
brawling fighting
council a group of people who discuss issues and make decisions
befall to happen to

Then said Telemachus, "If Zeus should grant that I be king, I am ready to take up the kingship of the land of Ithaca with all its toils and all its dangers." And when Telemachus said that he looked like a young king indeed.

The Council Meeting

As soon as it was dawn, Telemachus rose from his bed. He put on his **raiment**, bound his sandals on his feet, hung his sharp sword across his shoulder, and took in his hand a spear of bronze. Then he went forth to where the council was being held in the open air, and two swift hounds went beside him.

The chief men of the land of Ithaca were gathered for the council. When all were there, the man who was oldest among them, the lord Aegyptus, rose up and spoke. "Never since Odysseus **summoned** us together before he took ship for the war of Troy have we met in council," said he. "Why have we been brought together now? Has someone heard tidings of the return of Odysseus?"

Telemachus rose up to speak and the herald put a staff into his hands as a sign that he was to be listened to with

---

raiment clothing
summoned called; sent for

reverence. Telemachus then spoke, addressing the old lord Aegyptus.

"I will tell you who it is," he said, "who has called the men of Ithaca together in council, and for what purpose. I have called you together, but not because I have had tidings of the return of my father, the renowned Odysseus,

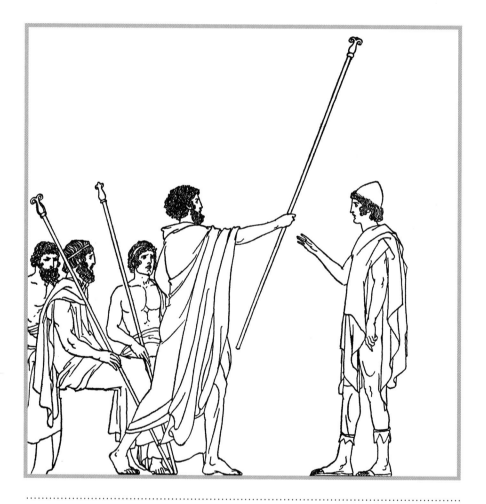

....

reverence great respect; honor

nor because I would speak to you about some affair of our country. No. I would speak to you all because I suffer and because I am at a loss. You have lost your king, but you can put another king to rule over you. I have lost my father, and I can have no other father in all my days. And that is not all my loss, as I will show you now, men of Ithaca.

"For three years now my mother has been **beset** by men who come to woo her to be wife for one of them. Day after day they come to our house and kill and devour our beasts and waste the wine that was laid up against my father's return. They waste our goods and our wealth. If I were nearer manhood I would defend my house against them. But as yet I am not able to do it, and so I have to stand by and see our house and substance being destroyed."

So Telemachus spoke, and when his speech was ended Antinous, who was one of the suitors, rose up.

"Telemachus," said he, "why do you try to put us to shame in this way? It is not we but your mother who is to blame. We, knowing her husband Odysseus is no longer in life, have asked her to become the wife of one of us. She gives us no honest answer. Instead she has given her mind to a **device** to keep us still waiting. I will tell you of the council what this device is. The lady Penelope set up a

beset troubled
device a trick or scheme

great loom in her house and began to weave a wide web of cloth. To each of us she sent a message saying that when the web was woven, she would choose a husband from amongst us. 'Laertes, the father of Odysseus, is alone with none to care for him living or dead,' said she to us. 'I must weave a **shroud** for him **against the time** which cannot now be far off when old Laertes dies. Trouble me not while I do this. For if he should die and there be no **winding-sheet** to wrap him round, all the women of the land would blame me greatly.'

"We left the lady Penelope to weave the web, and the months have gone by and still the web is not woven. But even now we have heard from one of her maids how Penelope tries to finish her task. What she weaves in the daytime she unravels at night. Never, then, can the web be finished and so does she try to cheat us.

"She has gained praise from the people for doing this. Let her be satisfied with their praise, then. We will live at her house and eat and drink there and give orders to her servants, and we shall see which will satisfy her best—to give an answer or to let the wealth of her house be wasted.

"As for you, Telemachus, I have these words to say to you. Lead your mother from your father's house and to the house of her father, Icarius. Tell Icarius to give her in

---

shroud a burial garment
against the time to prepare for the time
winding-sheet a cloth in which a dead body is wrapped

marriage to the one she chooses from amongst us. Do this and no more goods will be wasted in the house that will be yours."

Then Telemachus rose and said, "Never will I lead my mother out of a house that my father brought her into. **Quit** my father's house, or, as I tell you now, the day may come when a doom will fall upon you there for your **insolence** in it."

And even as Telemachus spoke, two eagles from a mountain crest flew over the place where the council was being held. They wheeled above and flapped their wings and looked down upon the crowd with destruction in their gaze. They tore each other with their talons, and then flew away across the city.

An old man who was there, and skilled in the signs made by birds, told what was **foreshown** by the **combat** of the eagles in the air. "Odysseus," he said, "is not far from his friends. He will return, and his return will mean **affliction** for those who insult his house. Now let them make an end of their mischief." But the suitors only laughed at the old man, telling him he should go home and prophesy to his children.

....

quit to leave
insolence scornful disrespect
foreshown foreshadowed; predicted
combat fighting
affliction suffering; great hardship

Preparing to Embark

Telemachus went apart, and, going by himself, came to the shore of the sea. He dipped his hands into the seawater and prayed, saying, "O goddess Athena, who did come to my father's hall yesterday, I have tried to do as you bade me. But still the suitors of my mother **hinder** me from taking ship to seek tidings of my father."

Then he saw one who had the likeness of the wise old man, Mentor, coming towards him. But by the gray, clear, wonderfully shining eyes, he knew that the figure was none other than the goddess Athena.

"Telemachus," said she, "I have seen in you something of the wisdom and the courage of Odysseus. Hear my **counsel** then, and do as I direct you. Go back to your father's house and be with the suitors for a time. And get together corn and barley-flour and wine in jars. And while you are doing all this I will gather together a crew for your ship. There are many ships in **sea-girt** Ithaca and I shall choose the best for you and we will rig her quickly and launch her on the wide deep."

When Telemachus heard her counsel he **tarried** no more but went back to the house and down into the

....

embark to set out on a voyage; to board a ship
hinder to hold back; to get in the way of
counsel advice
sea-girt surrounded by the sea
tarried waited; delayed

treasure-vault. It was a spacious room filled with gold and bronze and chests of raiment and casks of wine. The doors of that vault were closed night and day. Eurycleia, who had been the nurse of Telemachus when he was little, guarded the place. She came to him, and he spoke to her:

"My nurse," said he, "none but yourself must know what I would do now, and you must swear not to speak of it to my lady-mother until twelve days from this. Fill twelve jars with wine for me now, and pour twelve measures of barley-meal into well-sewn skins. Leave them all together for me, and when my mother goes into the upper chamber,

I shall have them carried away. Lo, nurse, I go to Sparta to seek tidings from Menelaus of Odysseus, my father."

When she heard him say this, the nurse Eurycleia **lamented**. "Ah, dear child," she cried, "how could you fare over wide seas and through strange lands, you who were never from your home? Stay here where you are well beloved. As for your father, he has long since perished among strangers—why should you put yourself in danger to find out that he is no more? Nay, do not go, Telemachus, but stay in your own house and in your own well-beloved country."

Telemachus said, "Dear nurse, it has been shown to me that I should go by a goddess. Is not that enough for you and for me? Now make all ready for me as I have asked you, and swear to me that you will say nothing of it to my mother until twelve days from this, or until she shall miss me herself."

Having sworn as he asked her, the nurse Eurycleia drew the wine into jars and put the barley-meal into the well-sewn skins. Telemachus left the vault and went back again into the hall. He sat with the suitors and listened to the minstrel sing about the going forth of Odysseus to the wars of Troy.

And while these things were happening the goddess Athena went through the town in the likeness of Telemachus. She went to this youth and that youth and

---

lamented wailed; expressed great sorrow

told them of the voyage and asked them to make ready and go down to the beach where the boat would be. And then she went to a man called Noëmon, and begged him for a swift ship, and Noëmon gave it her.

When the sun sank and when the ways were darkened, Athena dragged the ship to where it should be launched and brought the **tackling** to it. The youths whom Athena had summoned—they were all of the age of Telemachus— came, and Athena roused them with talk of the voyage. And when the ship was ready she went to the house of Odysseus. Upon the suitors who were still in the hall she

tackling equipment

caused sleep to fall. They laid their heads upon the tables and slumbered beside the wine cups. But Athena sent a whisper through the hall and Telemachus heard and he rose up and came to where she stood. Now she had on the likeness of old Mentor, the friend of his father, Odysseus.

"Come," said she, "your friends are already at the oars. We must not delay them."

They came to the ship, and Telemachus with a cheer climbed into it. Then the youths loosed the ropes and sat down at the benches to pull the oars. They set up the mast of pine, and they hauled up the sails, and a wind came and filled out the sails, and the ship dashed away. All night long Telemachus and his friends sat at the oars and under the sails, and felt the ship bearing them swiftly onward through the dark water.

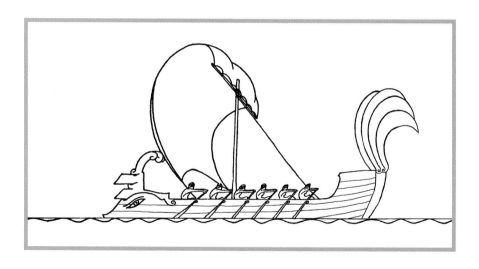

In the Hall of Menelaus

By sea and then by chariot Telemachus came to Sparta, to a country lying low amongst the hills. Telemachus **stayed** the chariot outside the gate of the king's dwelling.

To the king in his high hall came the **steward**. "Renowned Menelaus," said the steward, "there is a stranger outside, who has the look of a hero. What would you have me do with him? Shall I have his horses **unyoked**, bidding him enter the palace, or shall I let him fare on to another dwelling?"

"Why do you ask such a question?" said Menelaus in anger. "Have we not eaten the bread of other men on our wanderings, and have we not rested ourselves in other men's houses? Knowing this, you have no right to ask whether you should bid strangers enter or let them go past the gate of my dwelling. Go now and bid him enter and feast with us."

Then the steward went from the hall, and while he had servants unyoke the horses from the chariot, he led Telemachus into the palace. First he was brought to the bath, and when he had come from the bath refreshed, he was given a new cloak and **mantle**. When he had dressed he was led into the king's high hall. A maid brought water in a golden ewer and poured it over his hands into a silver

---

stayed stopped; halted
steward person who manages a household
unyoked freed from harnesses
mantle a loose sleeveless garment, worn over other clothing

basin. Then on a polished table the housedame placed bread and meat and wine upon it so that he might eat.

Menelaus came and said to Telemachus, "By your looks I know you to be of the line of kings. Eat now, and when you have refreshed yourself I will ask who you are and from what place you come."

But before the meal was finished, the lady Helen came into the high hall—Helen, for whom the kings and princes of Greece had gone to war. She watched Telemachus, and then the lady Helen said, "Menelaus, I am minded to tell you who this stranger is. No one was ever more like another than this youth is like great-hearted Odysseus. I know that he is no other than Telemachus, whom Odysseus left as a child, when, for my sake, the Greeks began their war against Troy."

Then Menelaus rose up and clasped the hand of Telemachus. "Never did there come to my house," said he, "a youth more welcome. For my sake did Odysseus endure much toil and many adventures. But Odysseus, I know, has not returned to his own land of Ithaca."

For many days Telemachus stayed in the house of King Menelaus. On the evening before he departed, Menelaus spoke to him of the famous deeds of his father, Odysseus.

"After we had taken and **sacked** King Priam's city," Menelaus concluded, "great troubles came upon us. Some

sacked plundered; looted; took the valuables from a captured town in wartime

of us sailed away, and some of us remained on the shore at the bidding of King Agamemnon, to make sacrifice to the gods. We separated, and the doom of death came to many of us.

"Of thy father, Telemachus, I have told thee what I myself have heard—how he stays on an island where the nymph Calypso holds him against his will: but where that island lies, I do not know. Odysseus is there, and he cannot return to his own country, seeing that he has no ship and no companions to help him make his way across the sea. But Odysseus was ever master of devices. And also he is favored greatly by the goddess, **Pallas Athena**. For these reasons, Telemachus, be hopeful that your father will yet reach his own home and country."

Later, Pallas Athena came to Telemachus where he lay in the **vestibule** of Menelaus's house. Telemachus was wakeful, thinking upon his father.

Athena stood before his bed and said to him, "Telemachus, no longer should you wander abroad, for the time has come when you should return. Come. Rouse Menelaus, and let him send you upon your way."

When Menelaus heard that his guest would depart, he told the lady Helen to bid the maids prepare a meal. He himself, with Helen his wife, went down into his treasure-chamber and brought forth gifts to Telemachus:

Pallas Athena another name used by the ancient Greeks for the goddess Athena
vestibule the lobby or front hall of a building

a two-handled cup and a great mixing bowl of silver. And Helen took out of a chest a beautiful robe that she herself had made and embroidered. They came to Telemachus where he stood ready to depart. Then Menelaus gave him the beautiful cup and the great bowl of silver, and beautiful Helen came to him holding the embroidered robe.

"I too have a gift, dear child, for you," she said. "Bring this robe home and leave it in your mother's keeping. I want you to have it to give to your bride when you bring her into your father's halls."

Then were the horses yoked to the chariot and Telemachus bade farewell to Menelaus and Helen who had treated him so kindly. As Menelaus poured wine out of a golden cup as an offering to the gods, Telemachus prayed that he might find Odysseus, his father, in his home.

The son of Odysseus turned the horses towards the sea and drove the chariot to where his ship was anchored. Then Telemachus gathered his followers, and he bade them take on board the presents that Menelaus and Helen had given him.

They did this, and they raised the mast and the sails, and the rowers took their seats on the benches. A breeze came and the sails took it, and Telemachus and his companions sailed towards home. And all unknown to the youth, his father, Odysseus, was even then nearing his home. ❖

How Archaeologists Found the Lost City of Troy

by Oscar Martínez

The recent discovery of Tenea, an ancient Greek city believed built by survivors of the Trojan War, continues the public's fascination with the epic tales of Homer, a trend started by Heinrich Schliemann, the passionate archaeologist who found Troy.

Heinrich Schliemann, the German archaeologist, was in Turkey in the late 19th century on an eccentric quest. He was excavating a tell—an artificial mound that covers long abandoned settlements. The site, known as Hisarlik, was familiar to only a few specialists. But as Schliemann dug, he was pinning his hopes on finding the ruins of the most famous city in classical literature: Troy.

The trouble was that Troy might not even have existed. The acclaimed Greek poet Homer popularized the Trojans and their city in *The Iliad* and *The Odyssey*, his 8th-century B.C. epic poems. These works told the story of a 10-year war between Greece and Troy, fought by such timeless characters as the kings Priam and Agamemnon, the warriors brave Hector and mighty Achilles, and the survivors crafty Odysseus and loyal Aeneas. The poems tell of bloody battles, fantastic adventures, heroic deeds, and tragic consequences. But was Troy a real place? Schliemann set out to prove it was....

And he did. Hisarlik is now widely accepted as the setting for Homer's epic tales. Studies have revealed that the 100-foot-high mound contains not just one, but nine Troys, each built over the ruins of the one before. Today archaeologists consider Troy VI—the sixth counting from the bottom up—to be the likeliest candidate for Homer's Troy. This city dates from around 1700 to 1250 B.C., and its citizens lived in **dynamic** times.

To their east was the waning Hittite Empire and to their west the mighty Mycenaean Greeks. Troy itself occupied a strategic location commanding the entrance to what is now the Dardanelles. Whoever held Troy would control the traffic along that busy commercial route, a fact that would not have escaped the attention of their Greek rivals.

The Roots of War

However, Homer's depiction of Troy revolves around passion not politics. It begins with the love affair between the Trojan prince, Paris, and Helen, the wife of the Spartan king Menelaus, brother to powerful Agamemnon, leader of the Greek forces. They **elope** to Troy triggering war between the nations and the decade-long siege that the Greeks bring to a terrible end with the famous ruse of the wooden horse. In reality, the motives for such a war were probably

dynamic lively; full of activity
elope to run off and marry in secret

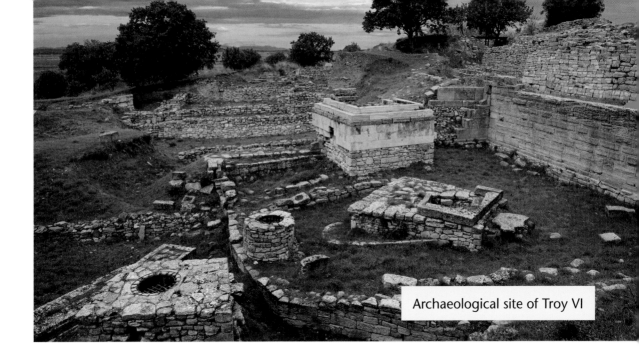

Archaeological site of Troy VI

more **pragmatic**. Whether or not there was a Helen, so beautiful that her face would launch a thousand ships, the commercial and strategic value of Troy made it a desirable target for any of its neighbors...

The citizens of Troy had anticipated outside threats. They had built a defensive wall and even dug trenches to stall war chariots, the assault vehicles of the ancient world. Trouble seems to have peaked around 1250 B.C. when the archaeological remains show signs of an attack and a devastating fire. But we cannot tell who the assailants were or if the destruction was caused by a single action or a series of onslaughts over time. Where the certainties of archaeology fade, we can only turn to ancient poetry for an account of the fall of Troy. And it's here that we find the

pragmatic realistic or practical

clever way the Greeks ultimately win the war and turn a proud, impregnable city into smoking ruins.

Homer's *The Iliad* foretells the fall of the city but stops short of recounting its actual destruction. In its sequel, *The Odyssey*, the end of the war is mentioned in flashback. Over the centuries other authors have added to the original tale, but only fragments of their works have survived. These include two chapters of *The Iliupersis*, a text possibly from the seventh century B.C., which refers to the ruin of the doomed **citadel**. More detailed accounts of the final days of Troy were written centuries later. These include Virgil's *Aeneid*, from around the first century B.C. and the *Posthomerica of Quintus Smyrnaeus*, written during the third century A.D. Quintus begins his story where Homer's Iliad leaves off: the funeral of Hector, the son of Priam and heir to the throne of Troy.

According to Quintus, the city seemed doomed after the death of Hector, Troy's greatest warrior. However, some Trojans kept hopes of a victory alive as they awaited the arrival of allies to help lift the siege. The first reinforcements are the Amazon warriors of Queen Penthesilea, but even they cannot hold the furious advance of the almost indestructible Greek hero Achilles. One of the most memorable accounts in the epic Trojan cycle is the duel between Achilles and Penthesilea: The Greek hero falls in love with his adversary at the very moment he fatally

citadel a fortress

plunges his spear into her side ...

Ethiopians follow the Amazons. The Ethiopia mentioned by Homer is a distant place on the banks of the mythical Oceanus River, perhaps identifiable with the Nile that had long supplied mercenaries to the Egyptian pharaohs. The Ethiopian army, commanded by King Memnon, now stands as the last line of defense between Achilles and the gates of Troy. The two warriors nobly agree to decide the battle by single combat. In the hot sun they dodge mighty blows from each other's spears, then switch to swords and Achilles at last finds a gap in his rival's armor. With one thrust he takes Memnon's life. Victory belongs to Achilles but it is short-lived. The Trojan prince Paris has watched the

The Many Layers of Troy

2700 B.C.
Troy (I) is found near the Dardanelles Strait. This first city seems to have been destroyed by fire.

2500–2300 B.C.
This site (Troy II) was initially identified as the city of Homer's tale by Heinrich Schliemann.

1700–1250 B.C.
Troy IV that thrived at this time is now believed to be that of Homer's legend. It had 6,000 inhabitants.

1250–1100 B.C.
After Troy VI is destroyed, the city is once again rebuilt (Troy VII). Two more will succeed it in Hisarlik.

8th century B.C.
Homer composes *The Iliad* and *The Odyssey*. In 1870 they inspire Heinrich Schliemann to hunt for the real Troy.

duel from behind the **parapets** of the city wall. Just as Achilles is about to storm the city, Paris, guided by the god Apollo, shoots an arrow that strikes Achilles in his one weak spot—his heel. (As an infant, his mother held Achilles by his heel as she dipped him in the River Styx, whose waters granted protection everywhere they touched. His heel remained dry, and therefore vulnerable to attack.) To the horror of the Greeks, their hero dies.

A Cunning Plan

Ten years of grueling warfare suddenly seem futile to the assailants: The Greek commander, King Agamemnon, orders retreat. It is at this moment of desolation and defeat that Odysseus steps in with perhaps the most famous *ruse de guerre* in history. Odysseus has the Greeks construct a huge and hollow wooden horse, which hides a small band of brave warriors. The Greek army fakes a retreat, sailing to a nearby island, and leaves the wooden horse on the beach as an offering. Odysseus's plan now hinges on the Trojans taking the gift within Troy's walls; once inside, the secreted soldiers will crawl out at night, overpower any guards, and open the gates. The Greek army, having returned under cover of darkness, will storm the city.

The plan is risky and there are no second chances. As dusk descends, the Greeks drag the horse before the city walls and abandon the camp they have occupied for years.

parapets low walls along roofs
ruse de guerre French for "trick of war"

That night the only Greeks left on the beach are those hidden in the wooden horse and a stooge named Sinon. As dawn breaks the following morning, the Trojan sentries see deserted tents, dead animals, and doused fires. They also spot something else: a magnificent wooden horse. King Priam orders the gates to be opened, and for the first time in a decade the Trojans were able to walk freely outside of their city—many flocked to admire the unusual offering.

Enter Sinon, dramatically throwing himself at the mercy of the Trojans. He spins a story of having deserted the Greek ranks because they had chosen him to be a human sacrifice. Sinon assures his new friends that the horse is a gift to the gods to ensure a safe return journey home. He adds that the horse has special powers and whoever possesses it will never suffer defeat.

Open Doors, Suspicious Minds

After a decade of war this news falls like rain on parched soil, and the Trojans lap it up. But Laocoön, the priest of Apollo, suspects a trick. When his impassioned pleas are ignored, he hurls his spear against the horse and snakes surge from the sea to strangle him and his sons. The Trojans interpret this as Poseidon, god of the sea, punishing Laocoön for **sacrilege**. Such dramatic divine intervention only reinforces the Trojan desire for the offering and soon the wooden horse is dragged within the walls.

sacrilege a violation of a person, site, or belief considered to be sacred

Even now, the Greek plan can go disastrously wrong, as Helen is also suspicious. She approaches the horse, imitating the voices of Greek wives in an attempt to provoke a reaction from any lovesick warriors within. Inside, Odysseus sees the ruse affecting his men but keeps them silent, even "clapping his hand over the mouth" of one. And yet still the danger of discovery has not passed. Cassandra, a Trojan princess, cries out that the horse is a ploy and that the city will be taken. But the gods seem to remain with the Greeks, for Cassandra has been doomed to never have her prophecies believed. The Trojans celebrate their victory and as the **revelry** fades they take to their beds. The Greeks slip silently from the wooden horse, kill the sentries, and fling open the gates to the waiting Greek army.

Amid flames and blood, Troy falls and its defenders are slaughtered: King Priam is cut down with the rest of his army. According to Virgil, only one Trojan warrior escapes: Aeneas. With a burning city behind, he is depicted carrying his elderly father and clutching the hand of his son as they flee to Italy, where he will found a new Troy, the city now known as Rome. Meanwhile, Paris is wounded by a poisoned arrow to which only the nymph Oenone has an antidote. But it was she that Paris had abandoned for Helen, and despite his pleading, she refuses and he dies. As for Helen herself, when Menelaus raises his sword to deal

....

revelry merrymaking

the killer blow to his unfaithful wife, she opens her dress and reveals her body. Captivated once again, Menelaus spares her.

A Horse Is a Horse

The tale of Troy teems with memorable characters, but perhaps its most fascinating figure is the one that never speaks—the wooden horse. This has been frequently reimagined in literature, poetry, art, and cinema. Theories about the wooden horse abound. One proposes that it was a poetic representation of the wooden ships on which the Greeks arrived that evolved into a tangible aspect of the myth. Another suggests that a Trojan betrayed the city, sketching a horse on a secret gate as a sign to the Greeks. Others point out that horses were closely linked to the god Poseidon, sometimes known as "shaker of the earth." Does the animal represent an earthquake that caused the walls of Troy to fall?

Recent scholars have offered more pragmatic theories, including that the wooden horse was actually a siege engine. Such a device can be seen in an Assyrian bas-relief from the palace of Assurnasirpal II (883–859 B.C.) in Nimrod. This "Assyrian horse" postdates the destruction of Troy VI by several centuries, but written material from the archives of Hattusa—the capital of the Hittite empire—suggests such siege engines were in use as early as the 18th century B.C.

The device described was a portable wooden shelter around 26 feet in length and 6 feet wide from which hung a 17-foot-long pointed stake. Beneath the protective shelter besieging warriors would repeatedly slam the stake against the wall of the city to pry open a gap between the stones and weaken the structure. The Hittite documents refer to the device using animal epithets, such as "Savage ass" or "one-horned beast."

Thus the Trojan Horse can be rationalized as a siege weapon of **equine** appearance. But even if this is as satisfactory an explanation as we are ever likely to get, many questions remain: Who were the men attacking Troy? And who were the Trojans who fought so desperately, and so hopelessly, to save it from the flames? ❖

equine related to or resembling a horse

Which Is the Real Troy?

○ **1868**

Carrying a copy of *The Iliad* in his luggage, Heinrich Schliemann arrives in Turkey determined to discover the true location of Troy.

○ **1870**

After two years of frustration, and despite having no permit from the Ottoman authorities, Schliemann starts the dig. He discovers several Troys, each build on the ruins of the last.

○ **1873**

On reaching the city level of Troy II, he finds jars and a big building that he believes to be Priam's palace. In May he finds a horde of gold that he names the Treasure of Priam before smuggling it out of Turkey to Germany.

○ **1882**

Schliemann enlists the help of Wilhelm Dörpfeld, who continues the dig after Schliemann's death in 1890, Dörpfeld proposes that Troy VI, not Troy II, is the city immortalized in Homer's epic.

○ **1932**

Carl W. Blegen arrives in Troy and works there until 1938. He concludes that Troy VI was destroyed by an earthquake and not fire. Studying Troy VII, he discovers evidence of a conflagration and concludes that it could be the Homer's city.

○ **1988**

German archaeologist Manfred Korfmann begins excavations that continue until his death in 2005. Korfmann argues that Troy VI seems to be the likeliest candidate for the city of Greek legend.

Water Efficiency Strategies

*courtesy of United States
Environmental Protection Agency*

Drinking water systems can **implement** water efficiency measures and still deliver an unchanged or improved level of service to consumers while reducing overhead costs. Improving water efficiency reduces operating costs (e.g., pumping and treatment) and reduces the need to develop new supplies and expand our water **infrastructure**. It also reduces withdrawals from limited freshwater supplies, leaving more water for future use and improving the **ambient** water quality and aquatic habitat.

....

implement to put in place
infrastructure the physical structures necessary for a system to operate
ambient existing; already present

More and more utilities are using water efficiency and consumer conservation programs to increase the sustainability of their supplies. Case studies demonstrate substantial opportunities to improve efficiency through supply-side practices, such as accurate meter reading and leak detection and repair programs, as well as through demand-side strategies, such as conservation-based water rates and public education programs.

Supply-Side Strategies for Water Suppliers

Accounting for Water—Accounting for water is an essential step toward ensuring that a water utility is sustainable. This is best accomplished when water systems meter use by their customers. Metering helps to identify losses due to leakage and also provides the foundation on which to build an equitable rate structure to ensure adequate **revenue** to operate the system.

Water Loss Control—National studies indicate that, on average, 14 percent of the water treated by water systems is lost to leaks. Some water systems have reported water losses exceeding 60 percent. Accounting for water and minimizing water loss are critical functions for any water utility that wants to be sustainable.

....

revenue earned money or income

Demand-Side Strategies for Water Suppliers

Water Rates—One of the most effective ways to reduce demand for water is to establish rates that escalate as more water is used.

Consumer Efficiency—Consumers can reduce water use by installing water-efficient products or employing efficiency practices, such as turning the water off while brushing teeth or running washing machines only when they are full. Water systems can promote these actions through consumer rebate and education programs.

- **EPA's WaterSense Program**—WaterSense seeks to protect the future of our nation's water supply by promoting water efficiency and enhancing the market for water-efficient products, programs, and practices. Visit the website for information on water-efficient products and practices, as well as utilities who offer rebates for WaterSense labeled products. Water systems can also apply to become a WaterSense program partner and receive tools they can use to promote their own water efficiency programs. ❖

Michael's Biography

courtesy of Centers for Disease Control and Prevention

Michael started smoking when he was 9 years old and his younger sister offered him a cigarette. Years later, Michael, a U.S. Army veteran, an Alaska Native, and member of the Tlingit tribe, would develop chronic obstructive pulmonary disease (COPD)—a condition caused by smoking that makes it harder and harder to breathe and can cause death. It wasn't until he nearly suffocated that he decided to quit smoking for good.

"Smoking was something I did to fit in," he says, remembering why he started smoking. "At first it was unpleasant, but the more I smoked, the more I became addicted to cigarettes." In the early days, he would hide the fact that he smoked and even smoked other people's cigarette butts. Even though Michael lost his father, sister, and many other people in his community to smoking-related diseases, he continued to smoke.

Michael served in the U.S. Army from 1977–1979. He smoked cigarettes throughout that period. Even though he

Michael, 57, from Alaska, diagnosed with COPD at age 44

made attempts to quit, he always came up with an excuse to start smoking again. At age 44, Michael was diagnosed with COPD. "I would wake up with 'smoker's cough.' That was a warning sign that I ignored," he says.

Michael was 52 years old when he made the decision to quit smoking for good. It was a day he says he will never forget. He woke up struggling to breathe. "It was 4 hours of **stark** raving terror. I was suffocating to death. Every cell in my body was screaming for oxygen!" He remembers riding in the ambulance, wondering if he was going to die. He never smoked another cigarette. "Losing your breath is losing your life force," he says.

Today, Michael continues to fight for his life. To help improve his breathing, he had lung volume reduction surgery. Diseased parts of his lungs were removed to help healthier lung tissue work better. After he quit smoking, his condition improved slightly, but his doctor says Michael needs a lung transplant. In his weakened state, Michael doesn't know if he would survive the surgery.

Michael enjoys the company of his daughter and two grandchildren but struggles with the thought of having to say good-bye. "I can't bear the thought of not watching them grow up," he says. "I don't know how to tell them." He wishes he had more energy to play with them. "I used to play volleyball and hike in the mountains, but I don't do that anymore," he says. "I avoid anything that involves running and carrying things. I stay away from smoke and exhaust. Now, it's all about friends, good memories, and living a little bit longer." ❖

------

stark complete or utter

Index of Authors and Titles

Acknowledgments

"Stopping by Woods on a Snowy Evening" and "Nothing Gold Can Stay" from THE POETRY OF ROBERT FROST edited by Edward Connery Lathem. Copyright 1939, 1967, © 1969 by Henry Hold and Co. Reprinted by permission of Henry Holt and Company, LLC.

"Raccoon Olympics" by Anna Chotlos. Reprinted by permission of the author.

"Charles" by Shirley Jackson from THE LOTTERY AND OTHER STORIES by Shirley Jackson. Copyright © 1948, 1949 by Shirley Jackson. Copyright renewed 1976, 1977 by Laurence Hyman, Barry Hyman, Mrs. Sarah Webster and Mrs. Joanne Schnurer. Reprinted by permission of Farrar, Strauss, and Giroux, LLC.

"The Necklace" adapted by Earl J. Davis from BIG BOOK OF DRAMATIZED CLASSICS, ed. Sylvia E Kamerman, copyright © 1963 by Sylvia K. Burak, reprinted by permission of PLAYS Magazine, Kalmbach Publishing Co., 21027 Crossroads Circle, Waukesha, WI 53187-1612. Web: www.playsmag.com

"The Bell Rock," Dr. P. J. A. Burt, Natural Resources Institute, University of Greenwich © Royal Meteorological Society, 2004.

"Latin & Soul" from MARACA: NEW AND SELECTED POEMS 1965–2000 by Victor Hernández Cruz. Copyright © 2001 by Victor Hernández Cruz. Published by Coffee House Press. Used by permission of the publisher.

"Mother to Son" and "Harlem [2]" by Langston Hughes from THE COLLECTED POEMS OF LANGSTON HUGHES by Langston Hughes. Used by permission of Alfred A. Knopf, a division of Random House, Inc.; also, of Harold Ober Associates.

"President Cleveland, Where Are You?" by Robert Cormier from EIGHT PLUS ONE STORIES by Robert Cormier, copyright © 1965, 1966, 1967, 1968, 1969, 1971, 1973, 1975, 1980 renewed 1992, 1993 by Robert Cormier. Used by permission of Random House Children's Books, a division of Random House, Inc.

"My Father Is a Simple Man" by Luis Omar Salinas is reprinted with permission from the publisher of THE SADNESS OF DAYS, SELECTED AND NEW POEMS by Luis Omar Salinas (Houston: Arte Público Press–University of Houston, 1987).

"Raymond's Run" by Toni Cade Bambara, copyright © 1971 by Toni Cade Bambara, from GORILLA, MY LOVE by Toni Cade Bambara. Reprinted by permission of Random House, Inc.

"Saving Tobe" originally appeared as Chapter One of Mary Bucci Bush's novel SWEET HOPE, published in 2011 by Guernica Editions Inc.

"The White Umbrella" by Gish Jen, copyright © 1984 by Gish Jen. First published in THE YALE REVIEW. Reprinted by permission of the author.

Image Credits